A Doubleday Activity Book

Follow the Dots

By Marjorie Thompson

DOUBLEDAY & COMPANY, INC.

Garden City, New York

ISBN: 0-385-03408-3

PRINTED IN THE UNITED STATES OF AMERICA

15   14   13   12   11   10

How to Use this Book

FOLLOW THE DOTS pictures are a lot of fun. They're easy to do. That's why all children like to make dot pictures.

Look for Number 1. Put your pencil on this dot and draw a line from Dot 1 to Dot 2. Then draw a line from Dot 2 to Dot 3. Continue in this way until you have gone through all the numbers. When you have finished, you will have a pretty picture.

After you have drawn the lines, there's still more fun ahead. Take out your crayons. Color the picture any way you want to. You can make it look very beautiful.

Jungle Shower

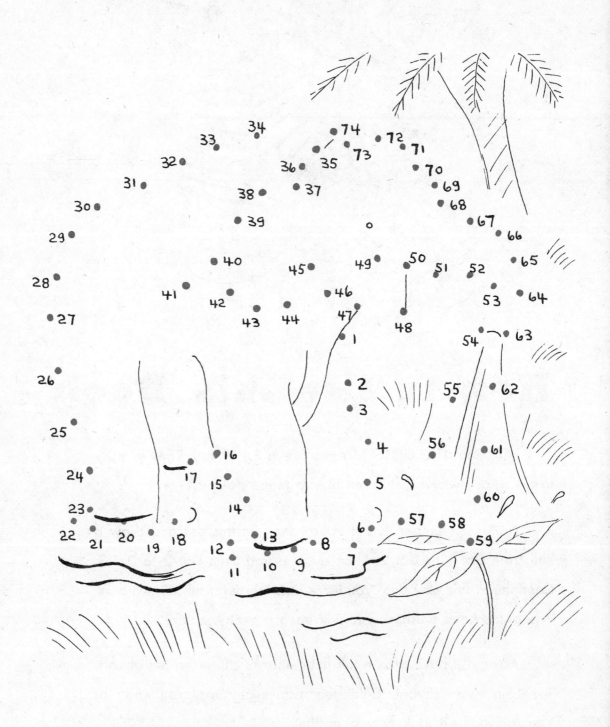

Big Fellow

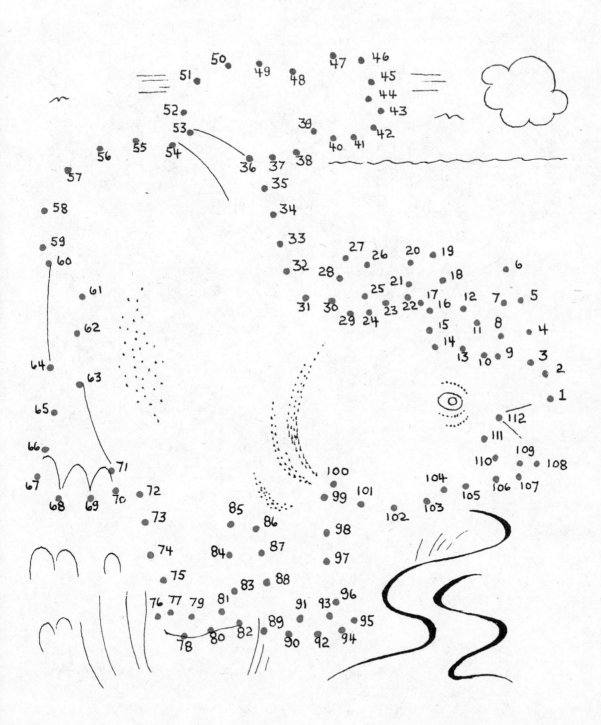

Surprise

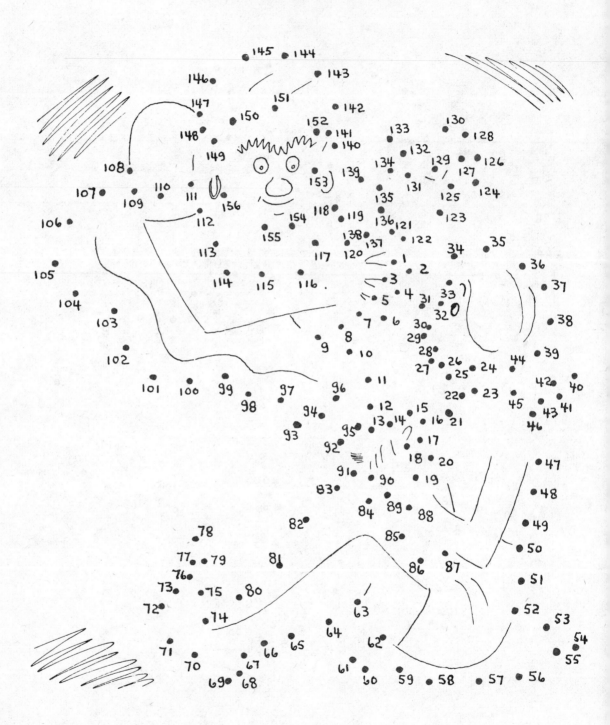

Autumn Meal

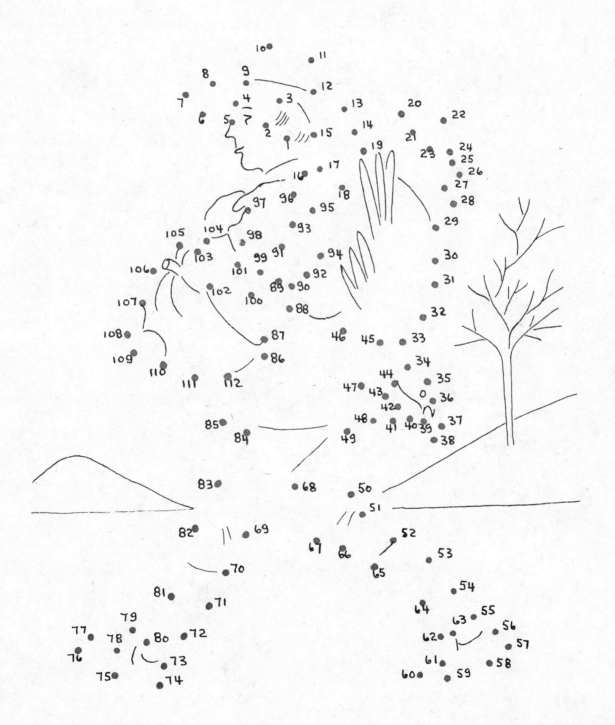

Friendly Neighbor

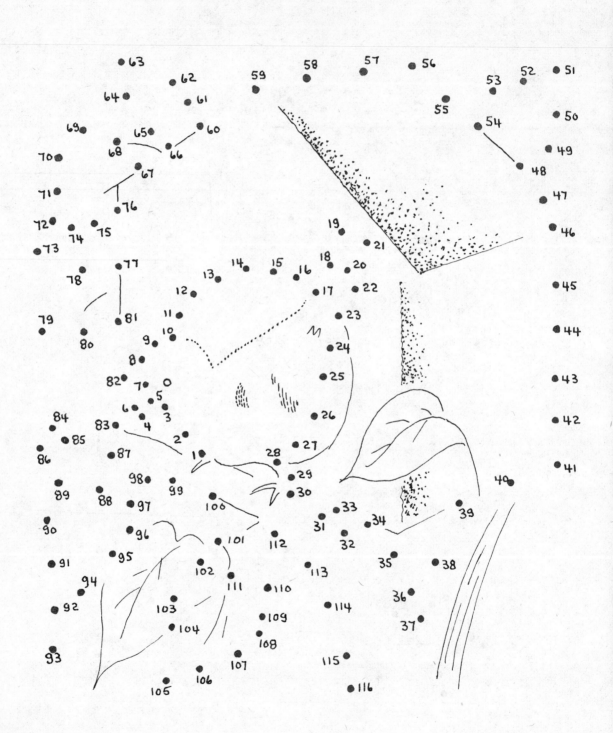

Early Dip

Free Ride

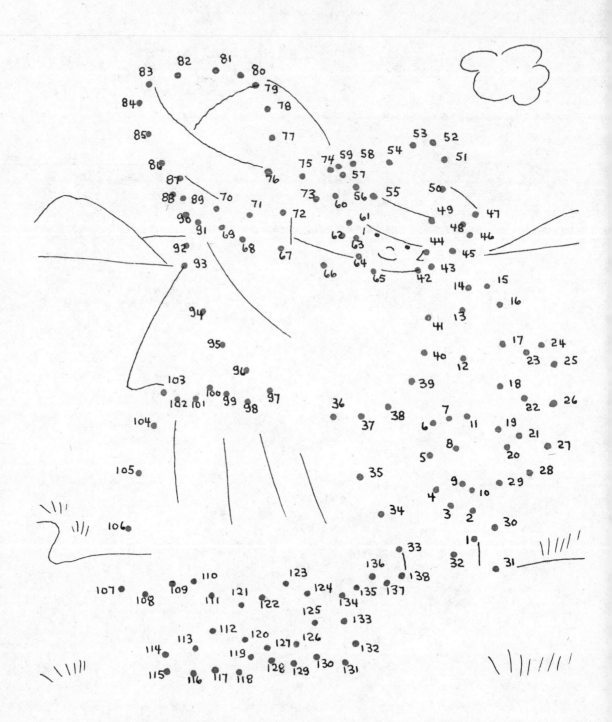

Troublemaker

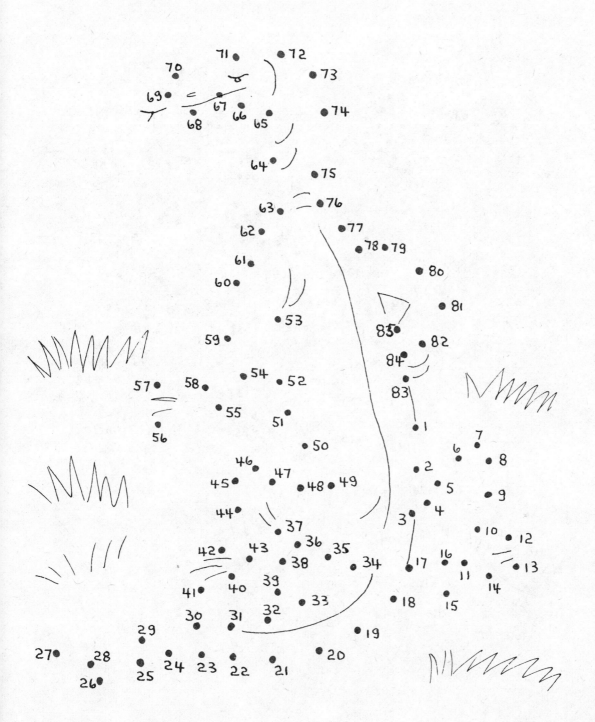

Mountain Tune

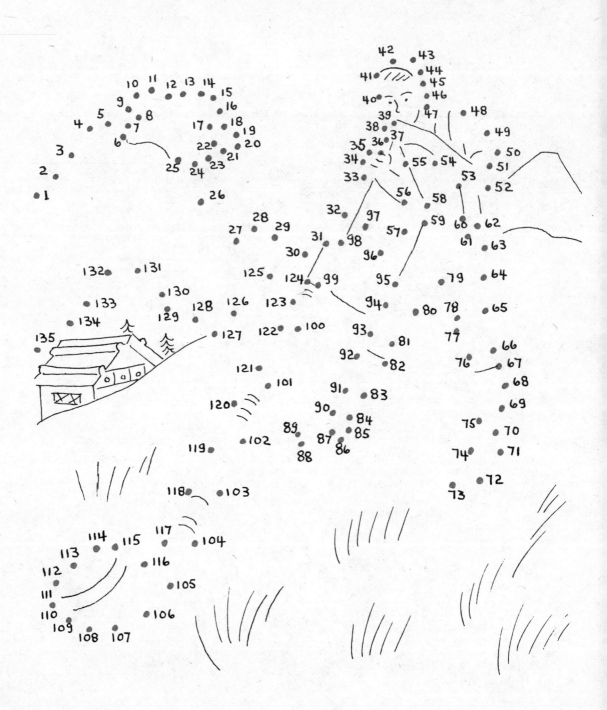

Bonnie Laddie

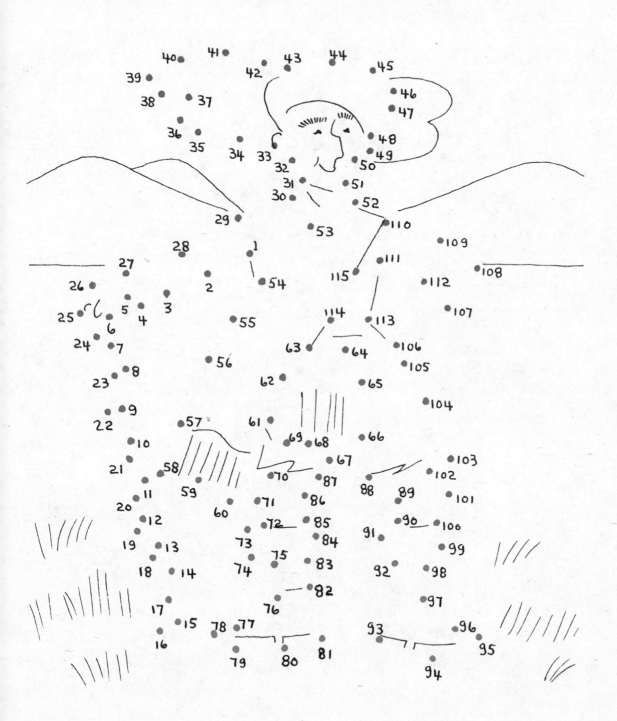

Mother and Child

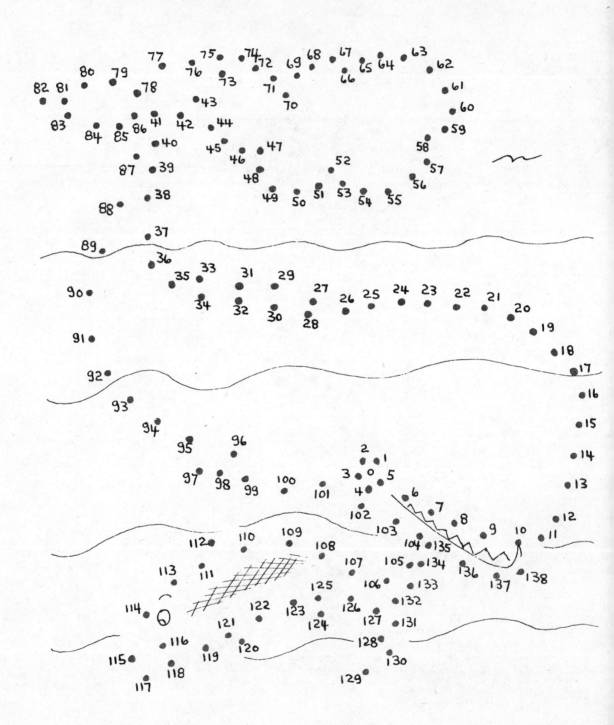

Delicate Work

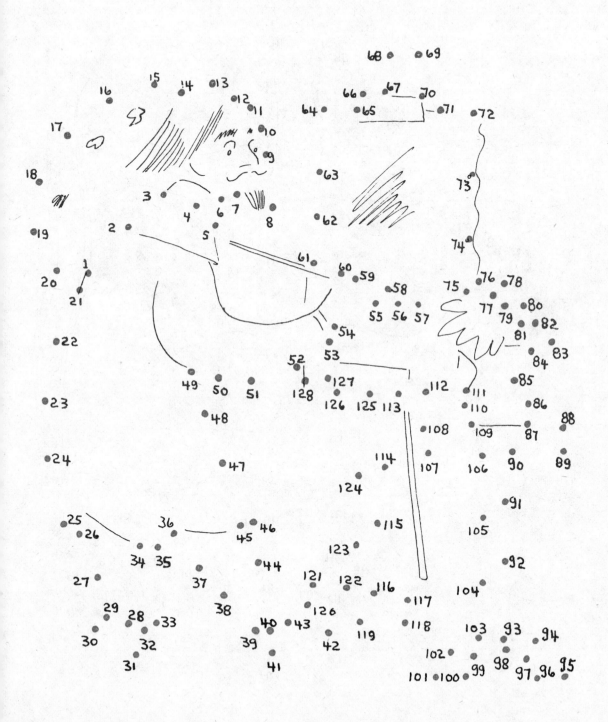

Champion Jumper

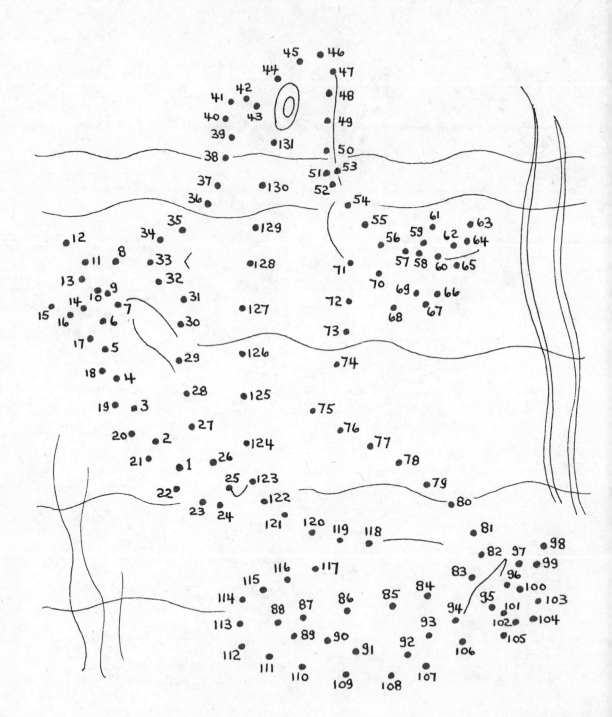

Up and Away

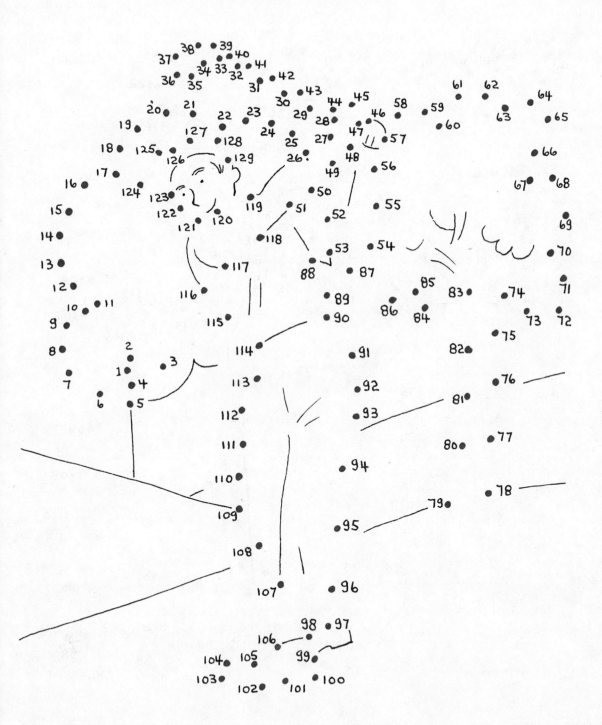

Good Morning

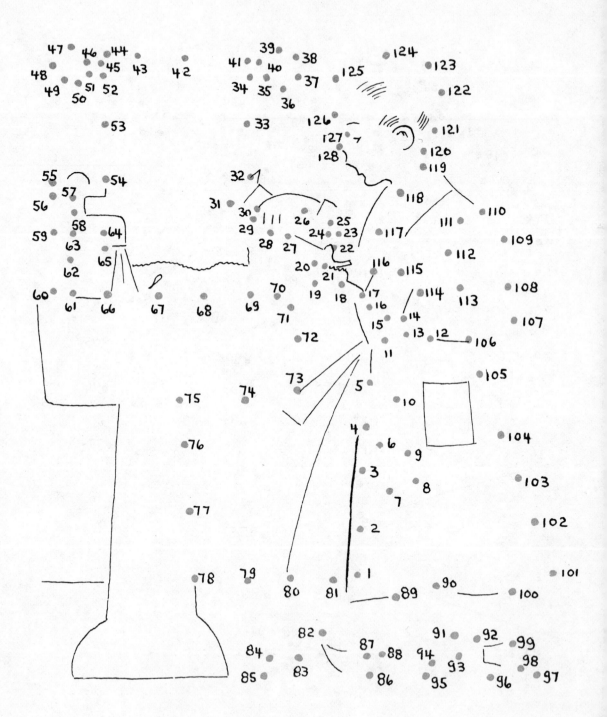

Up North

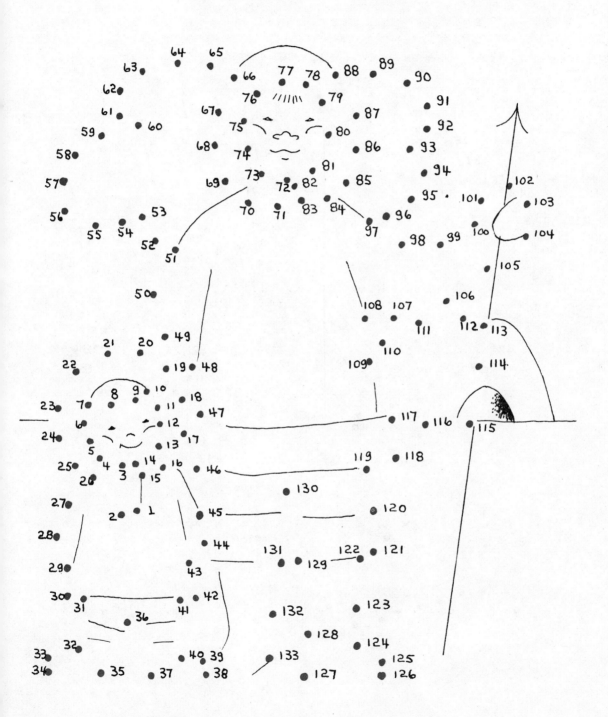

There She Goes!

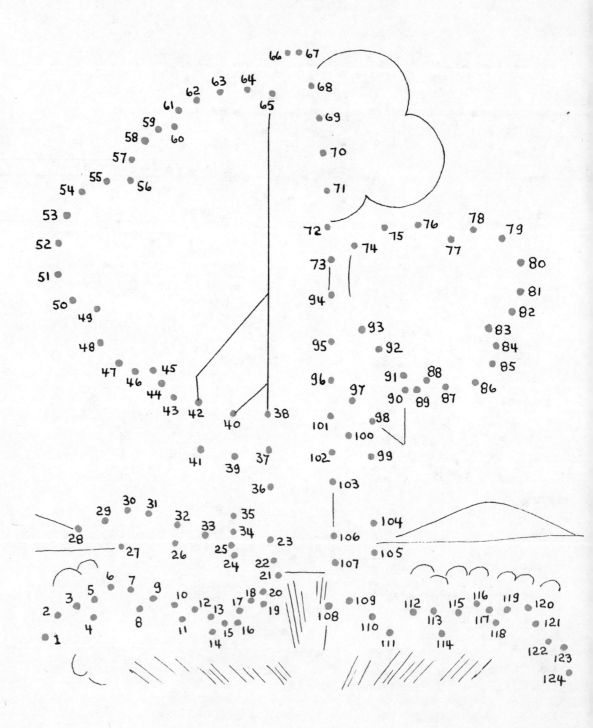

Stubborn

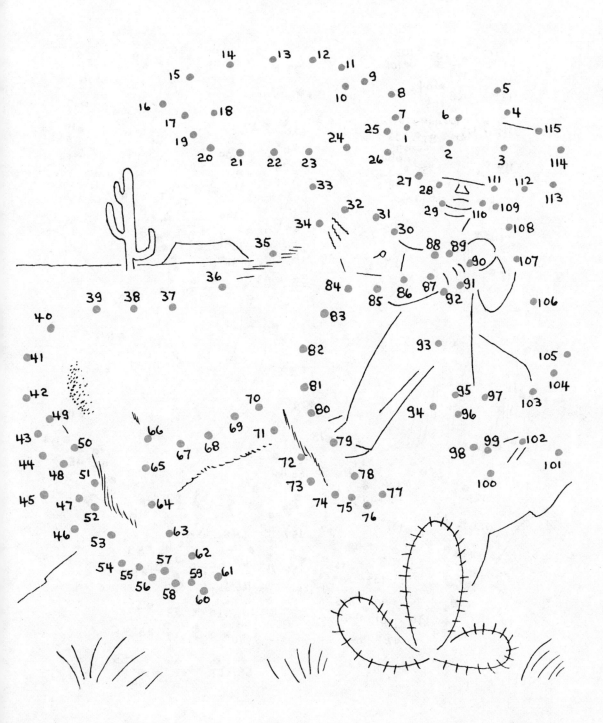

Over the Mountain

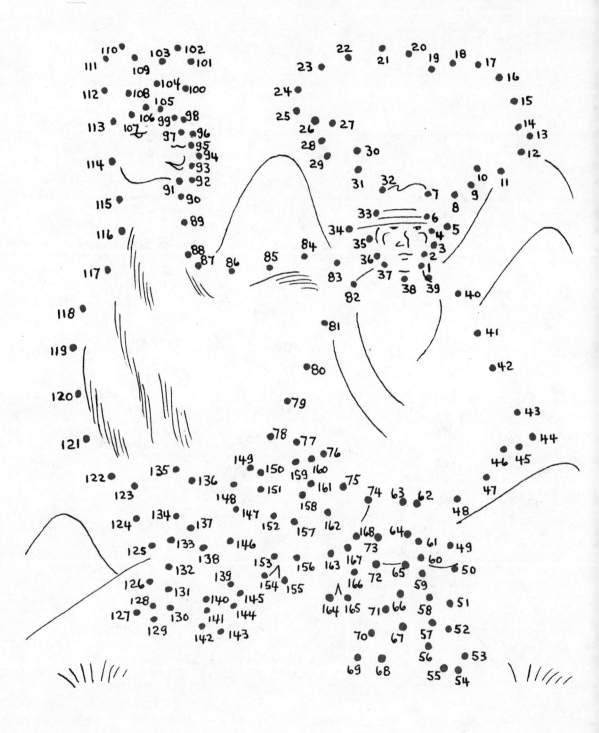

No Hurry

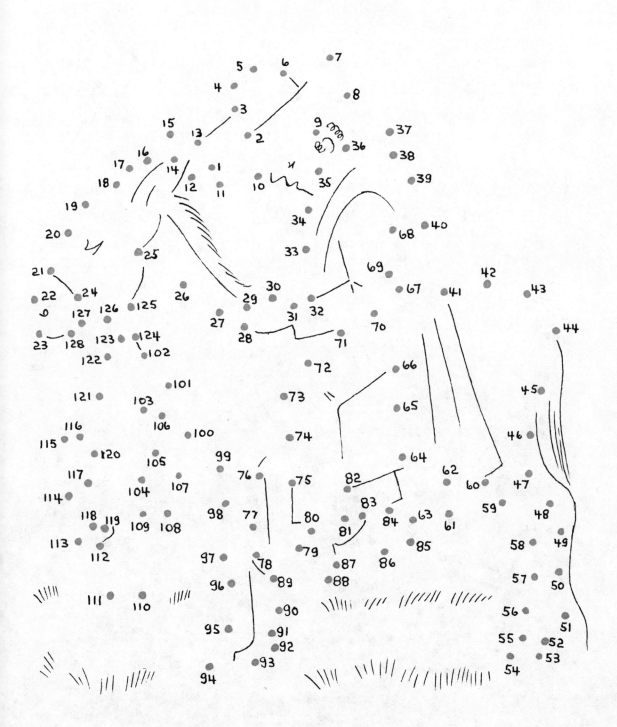

Watch Me

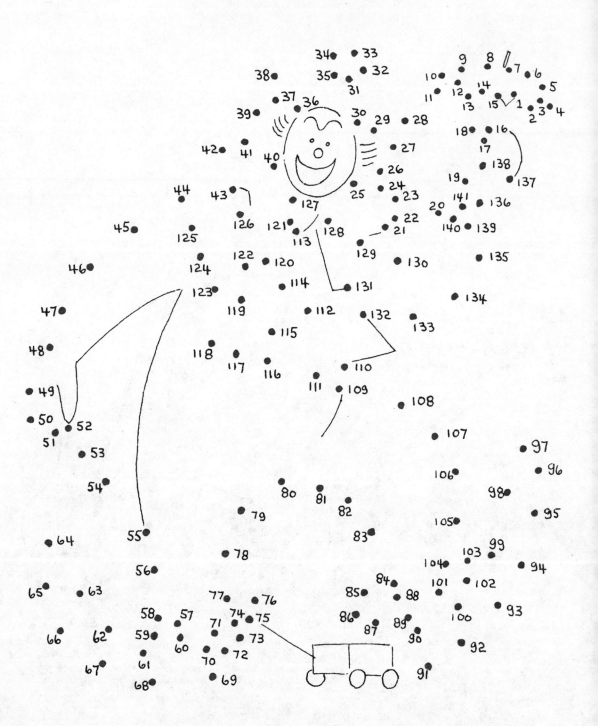

Winter Fun

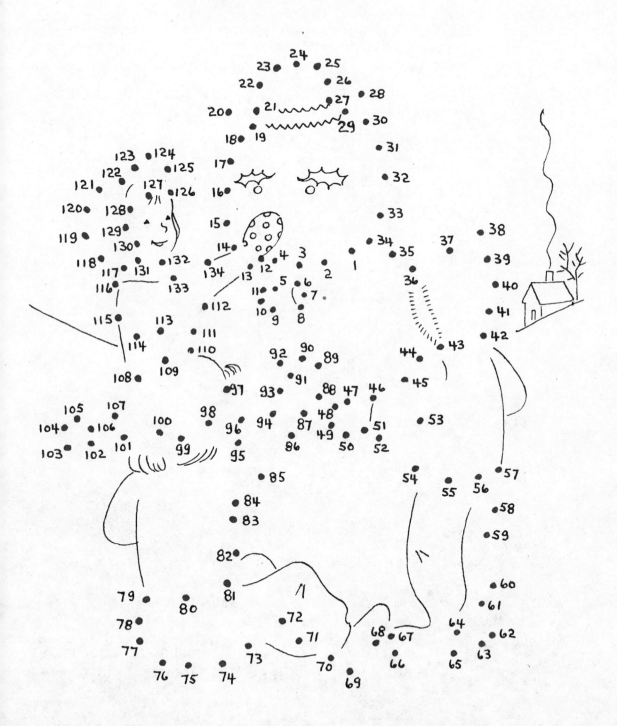

Some Fun!

Dessert Treat

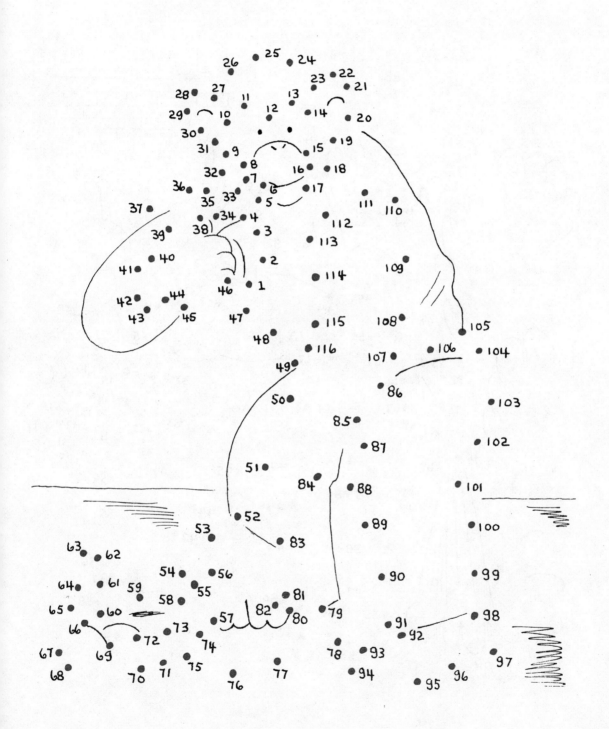

In the Garden

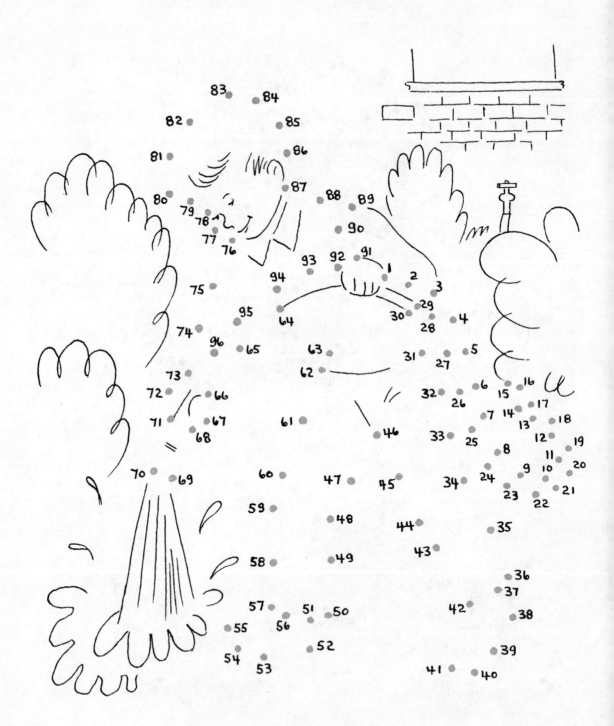

On Stage

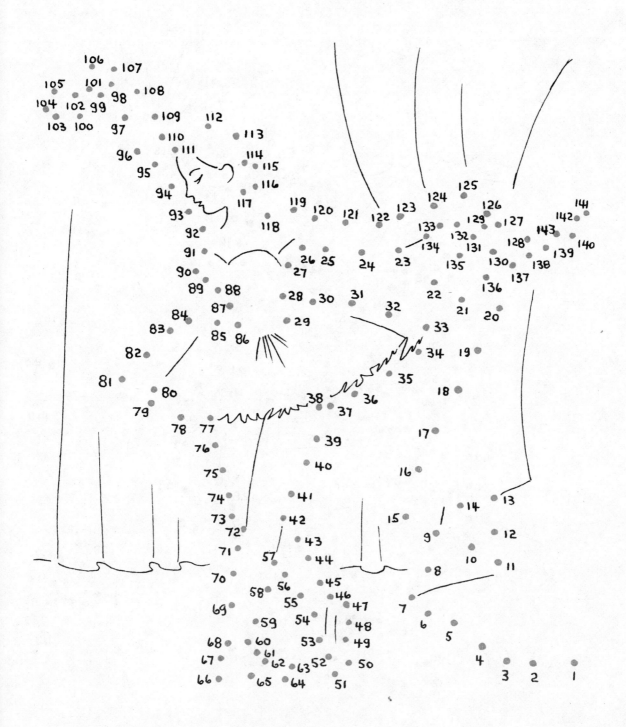

Loud Message

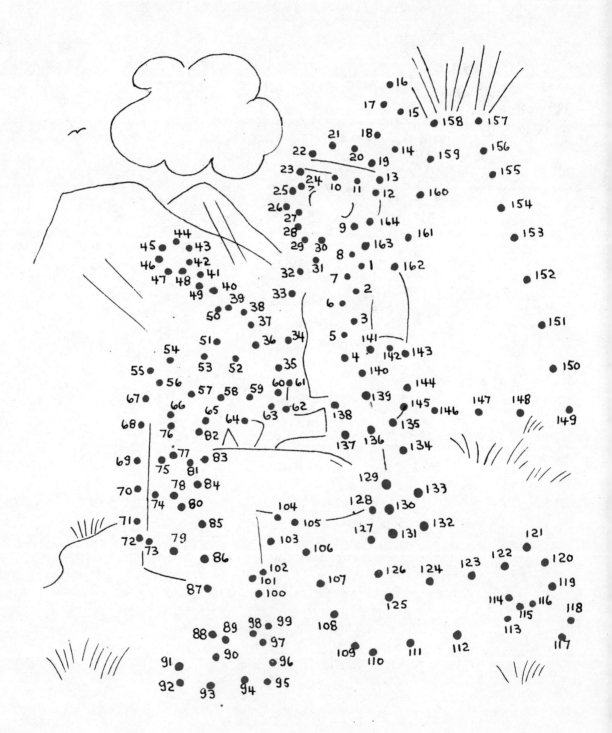

Under the Sea

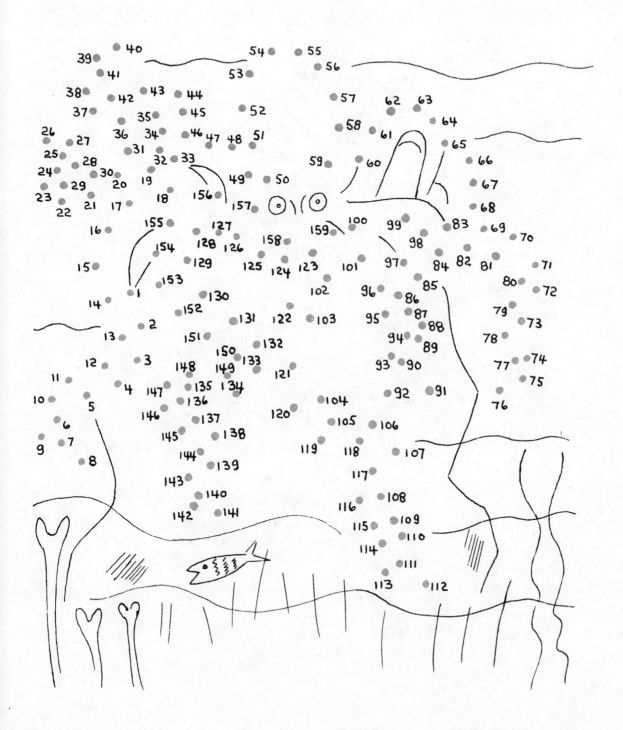

Icy Sport

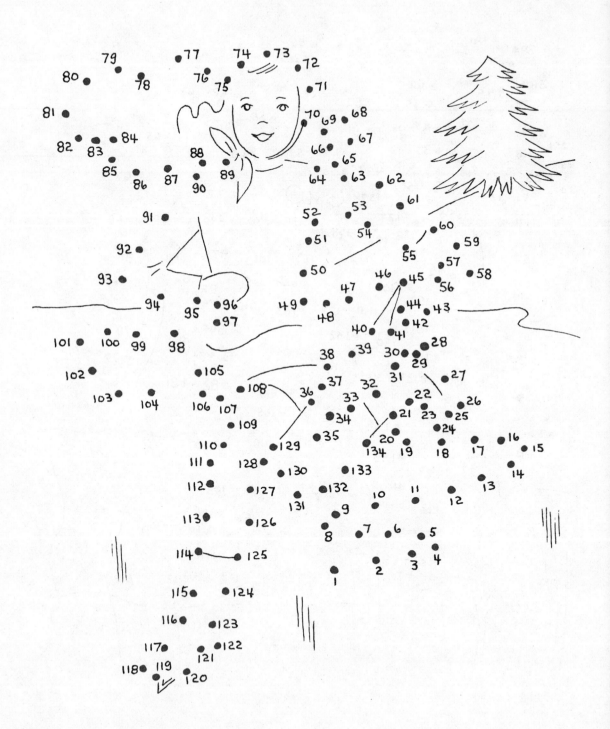

Winter Job

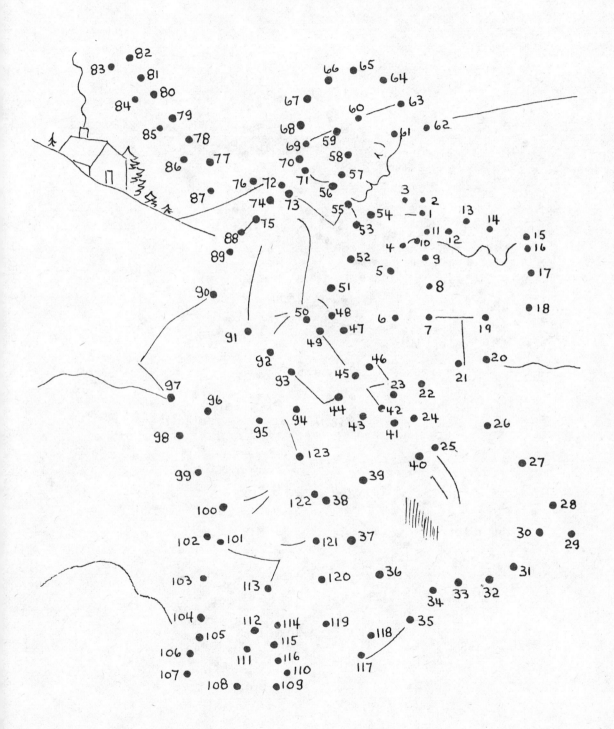

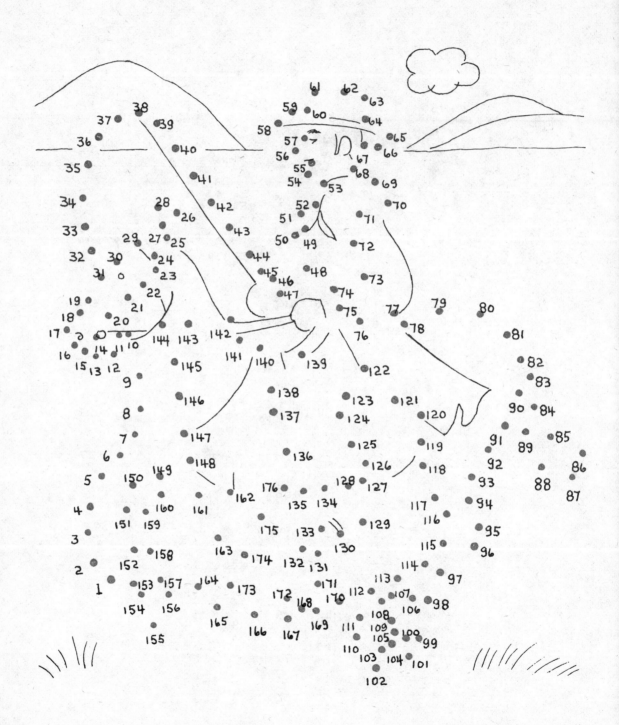

34

Happy Passenger

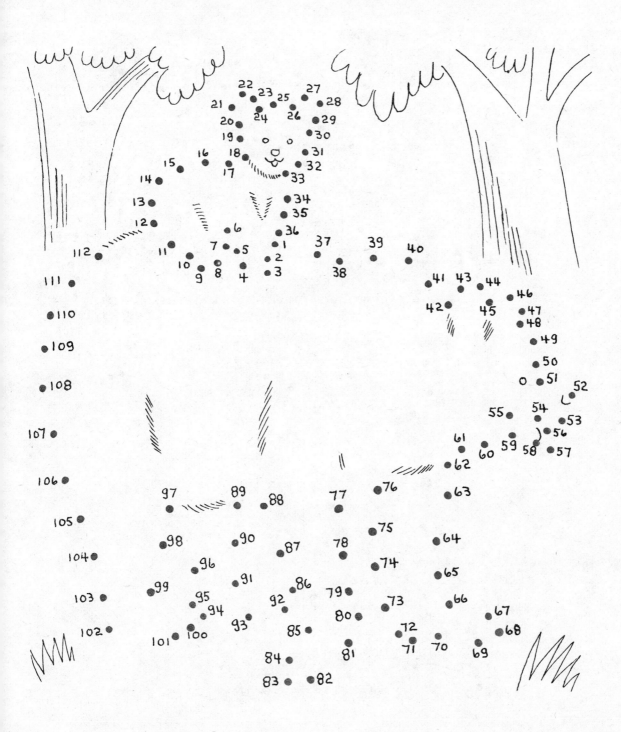

Far East

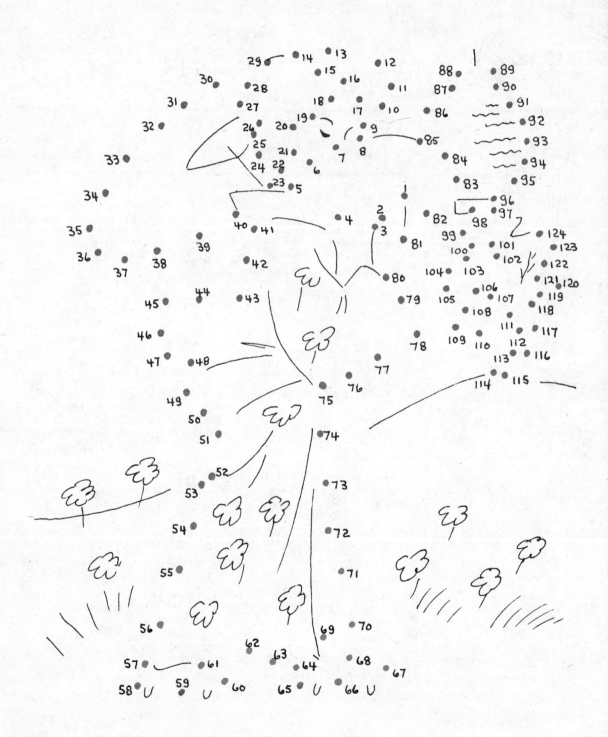

Sudden Leap

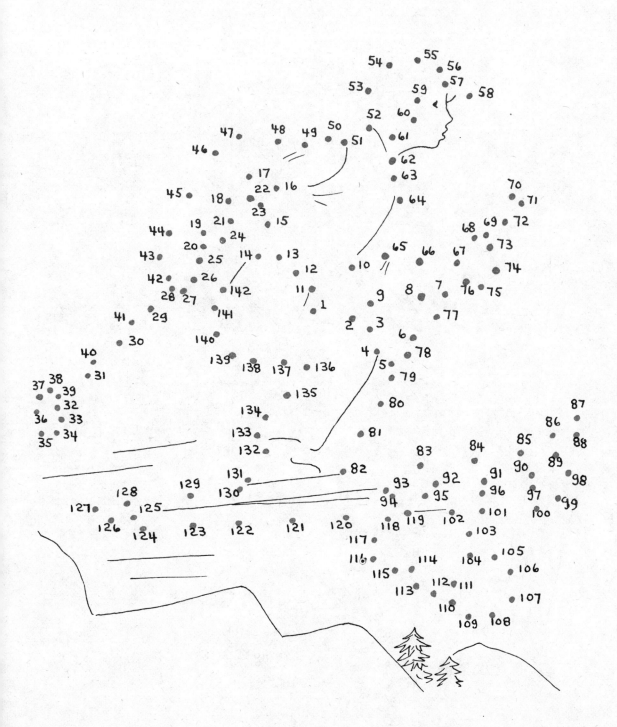

Out West

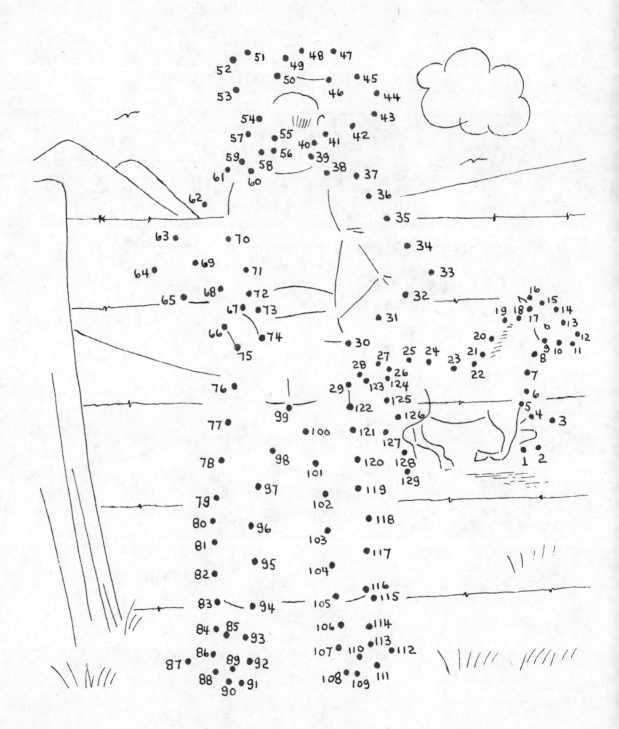

Come and Get It!

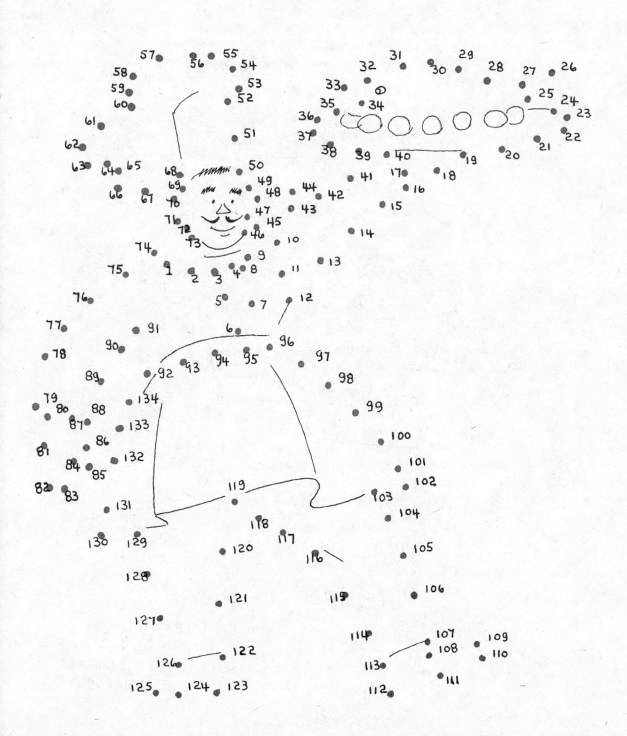

Which Way?

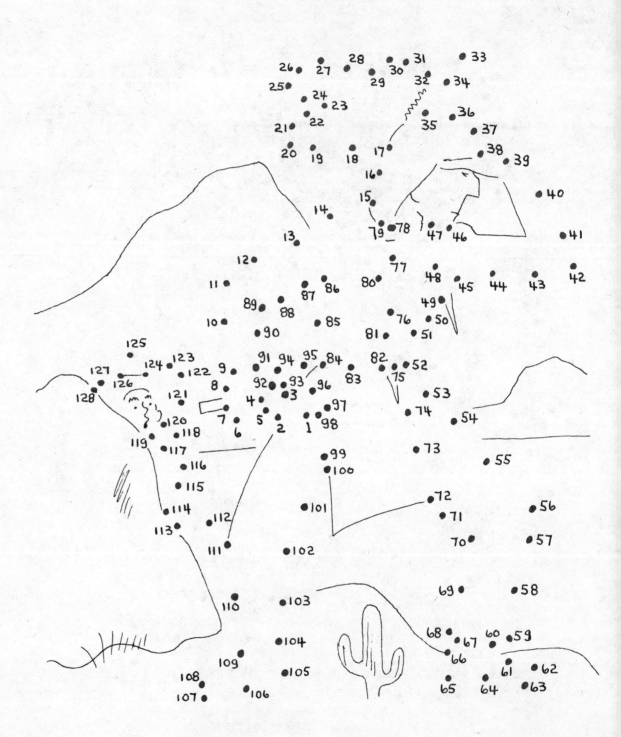

Back and Forth

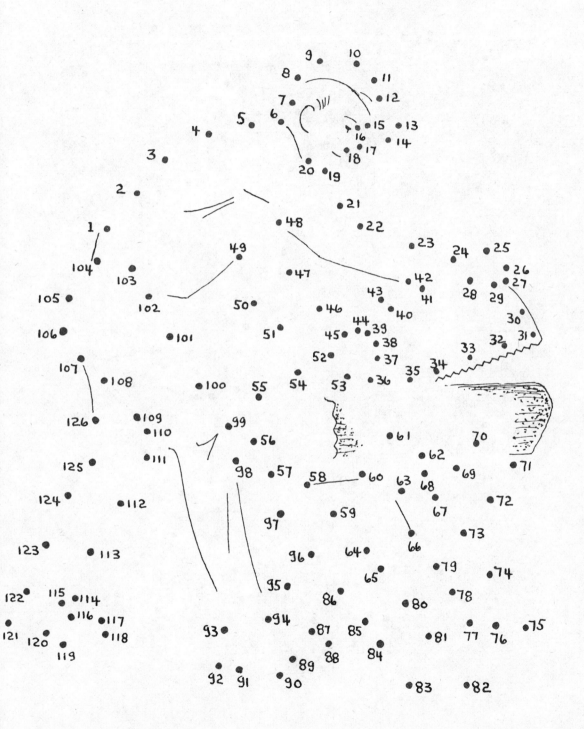

Circus Star

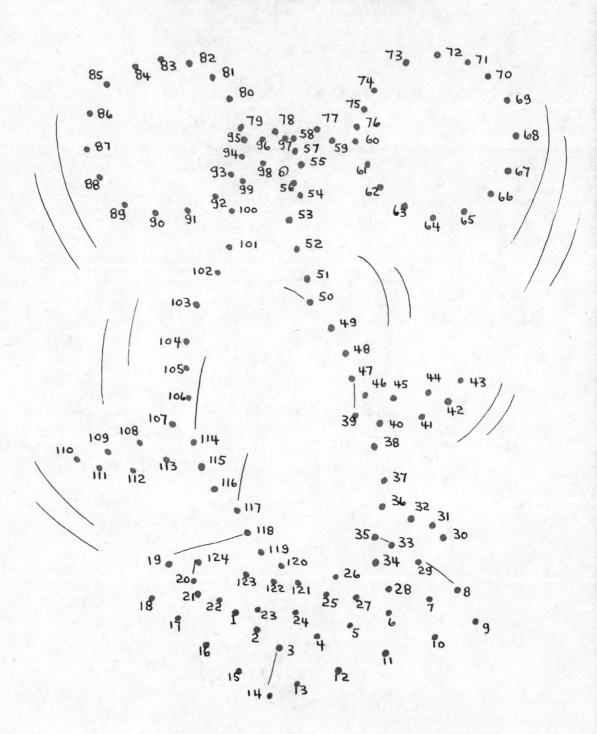

Up in the Air

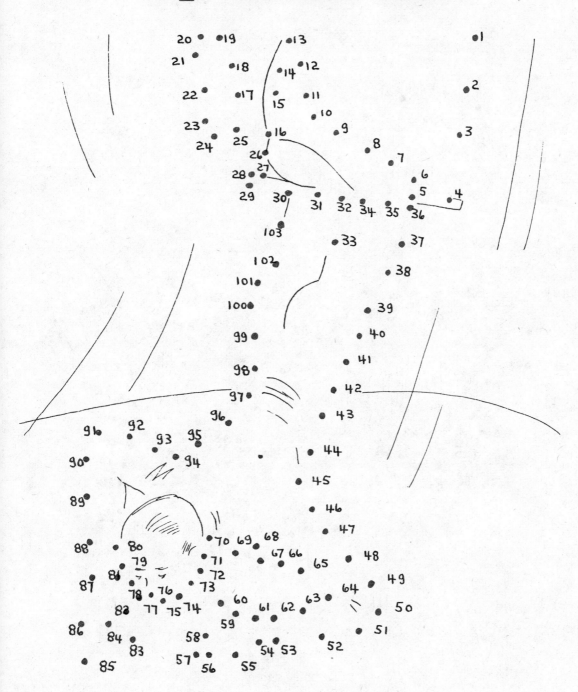

Time to Eat

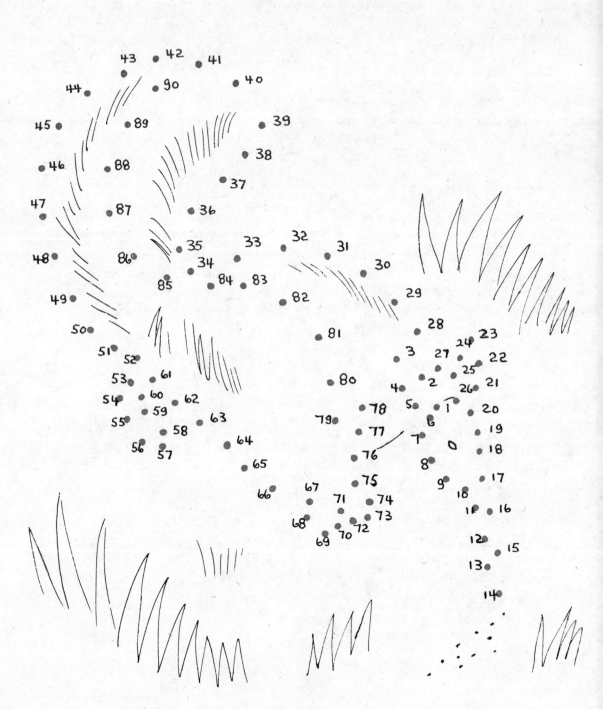

Unexpected Guest

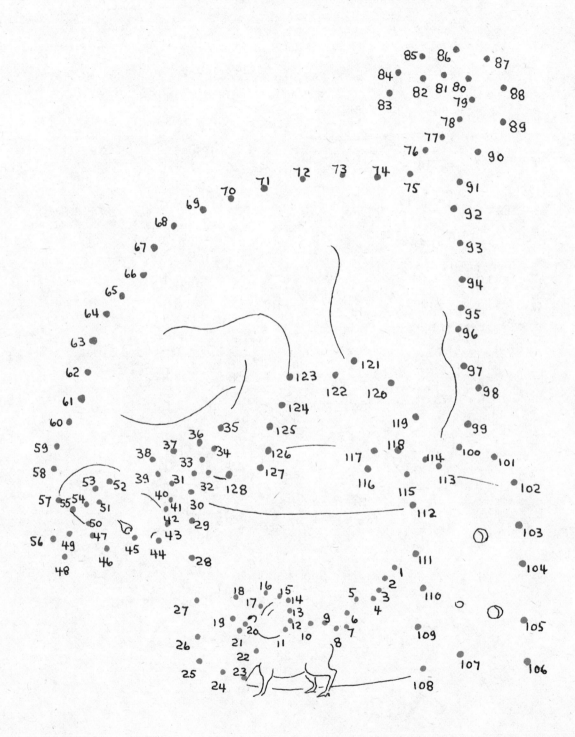

Light Snack

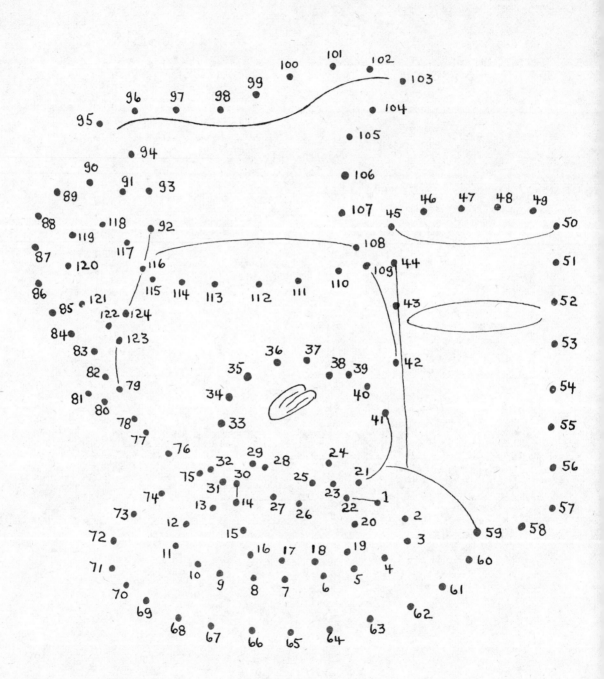

Big Mouth

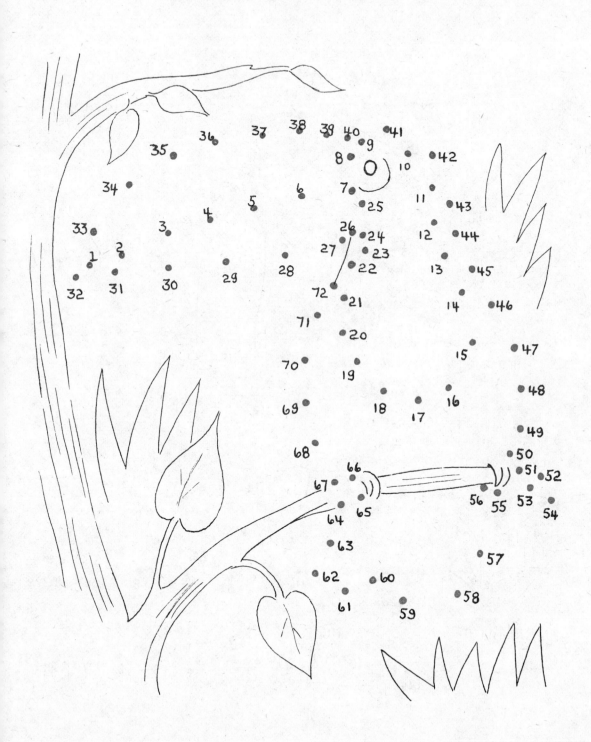

Helping Nature

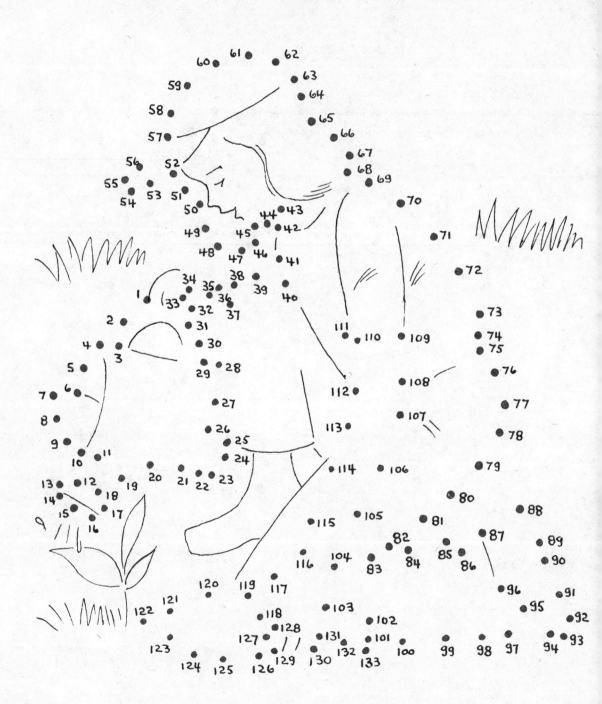

Pals

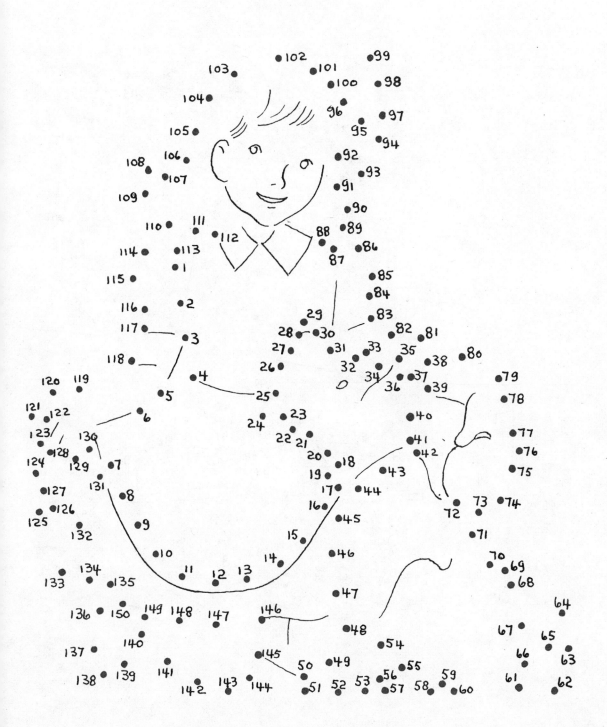

49

Out for a Ride

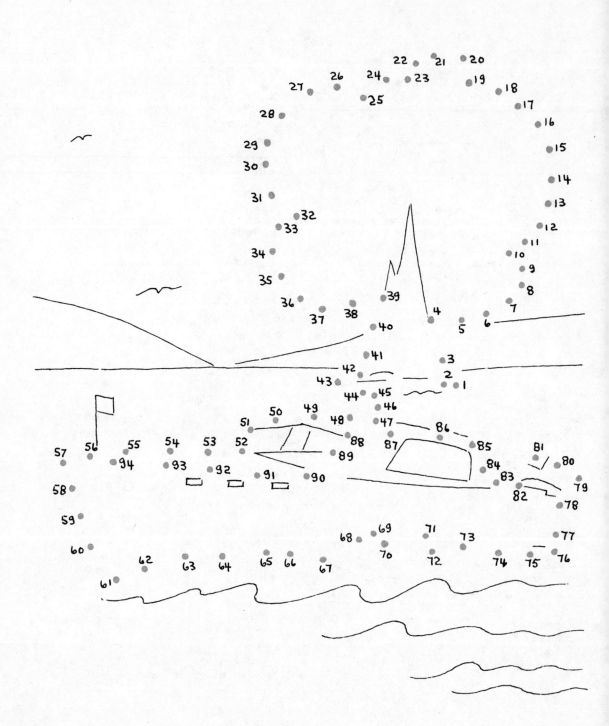

Big Bug

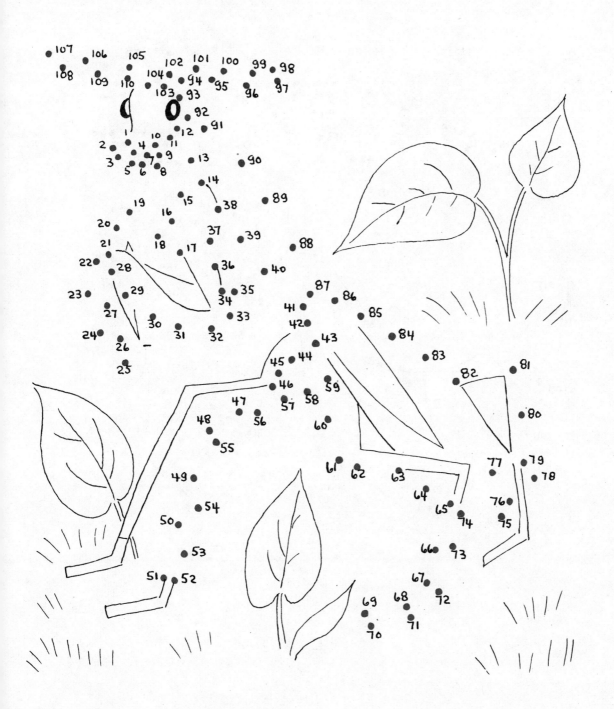

Big and Small

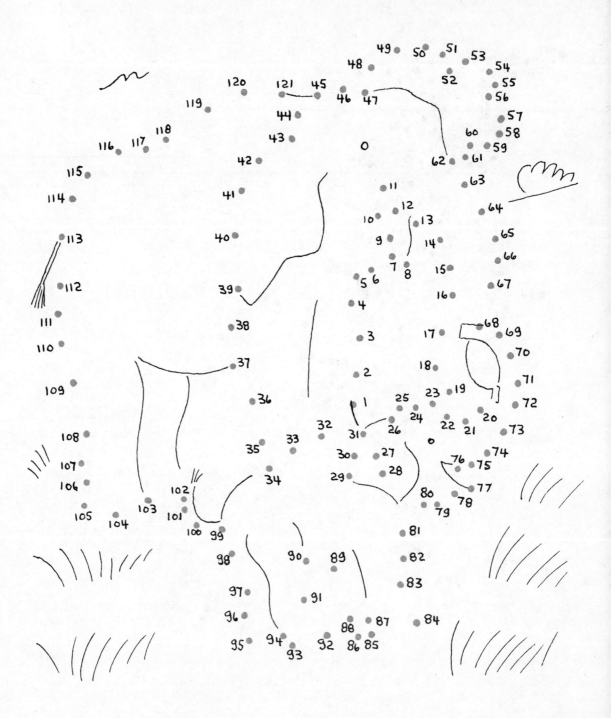

Slowpoke

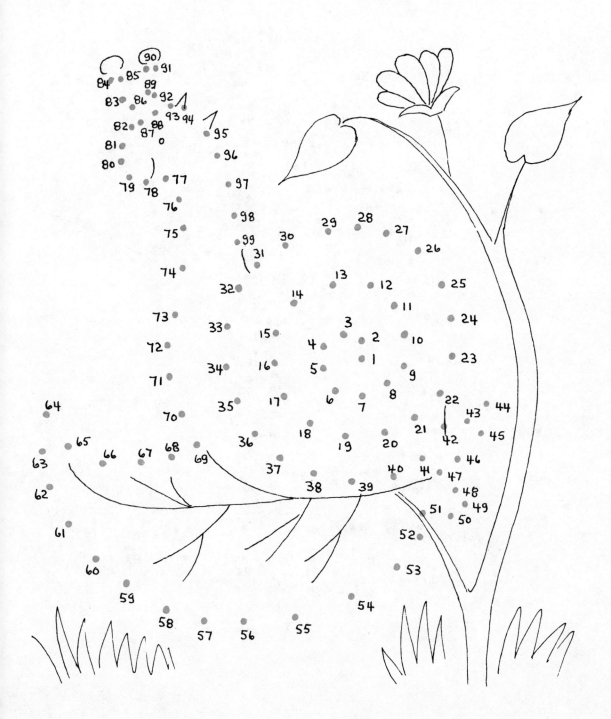

Tasty Tidbit

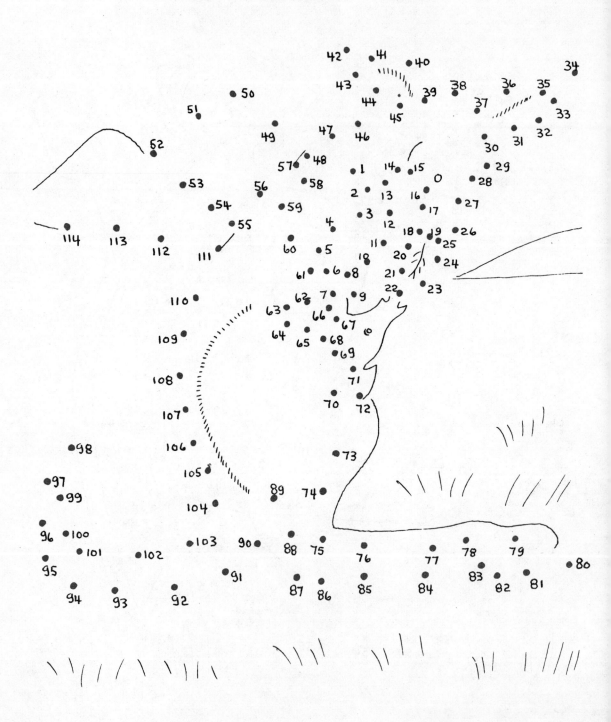

Temptation

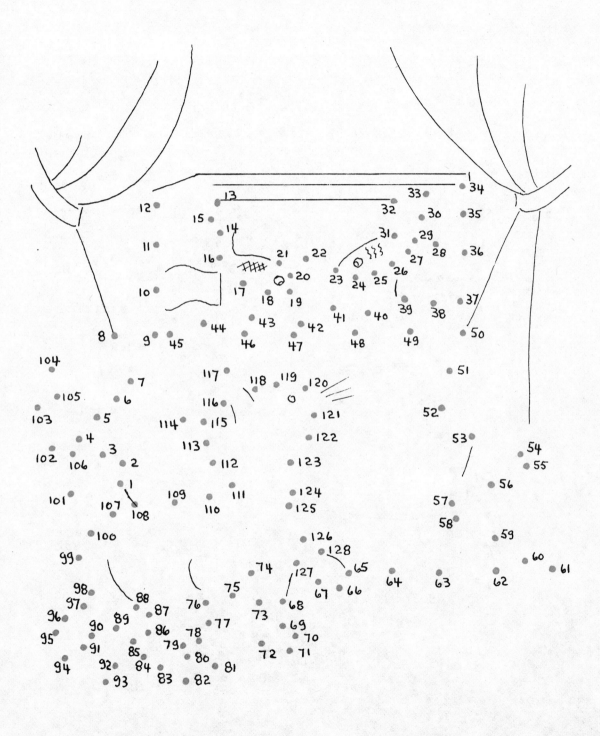

Guess Who?

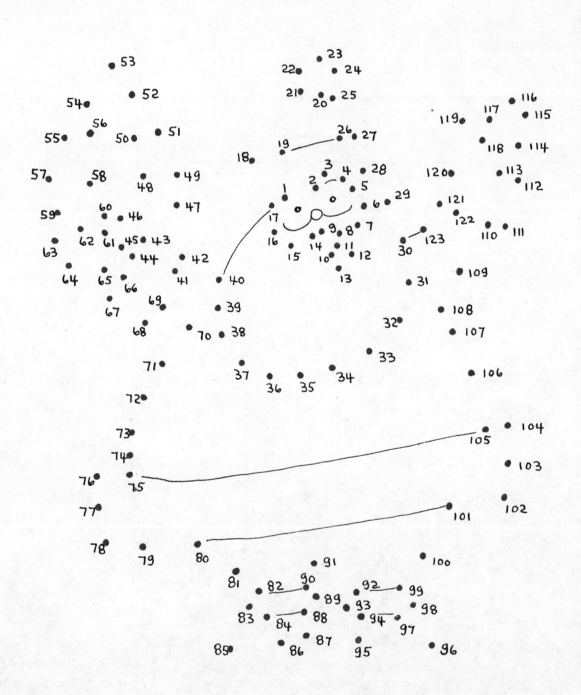

Where to Now?

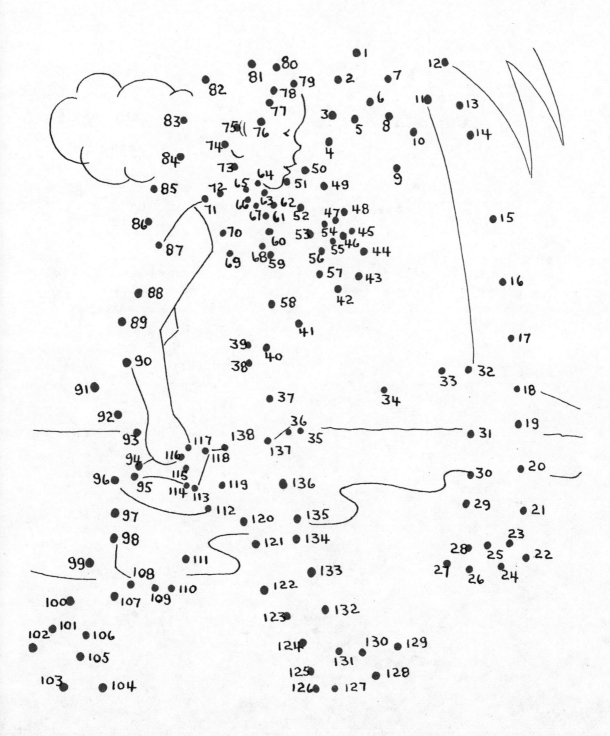

Easter Time

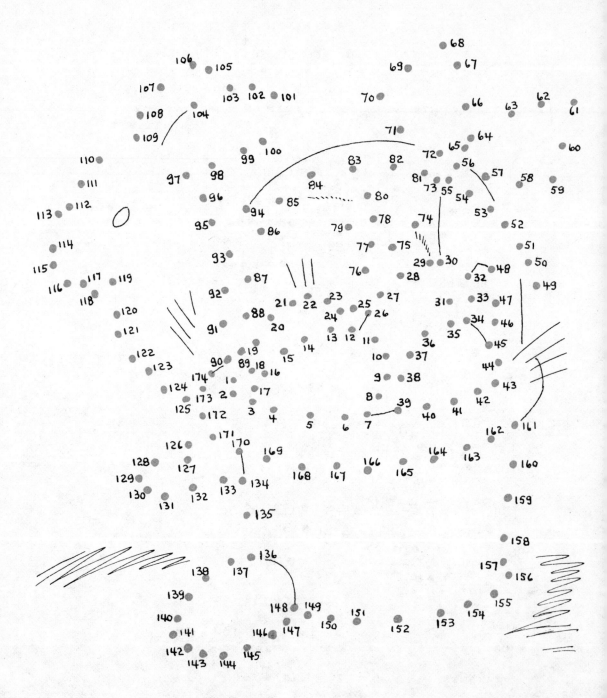

Stiff Breeze

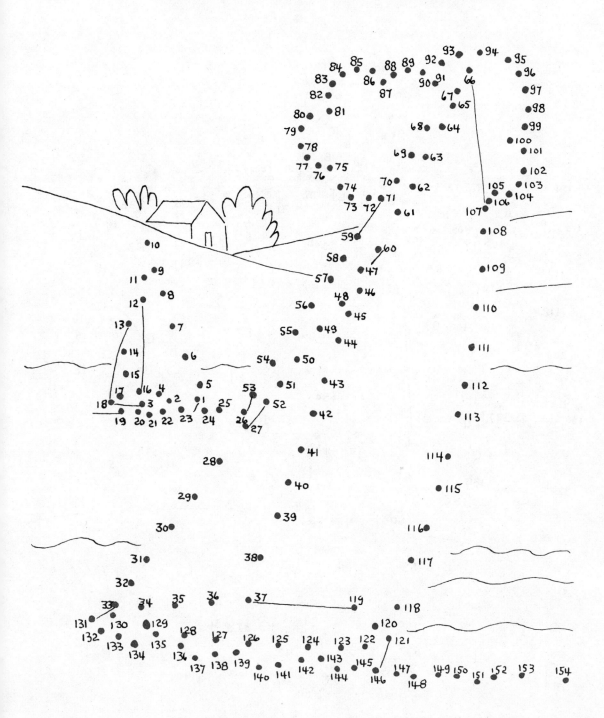

Perfect Balance

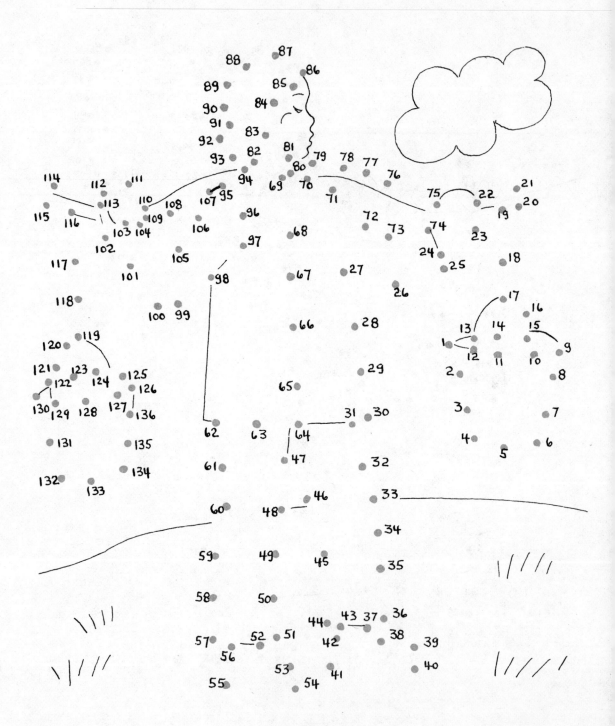

Making the Rounds

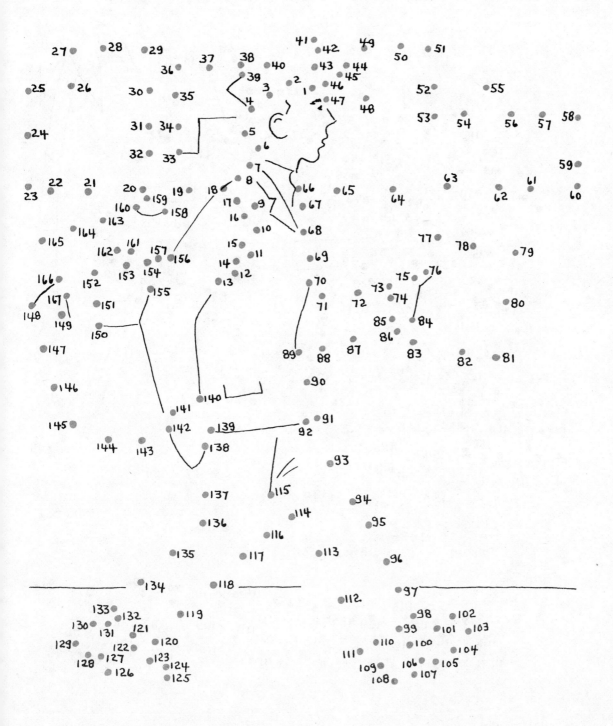

Pleasant Greeting

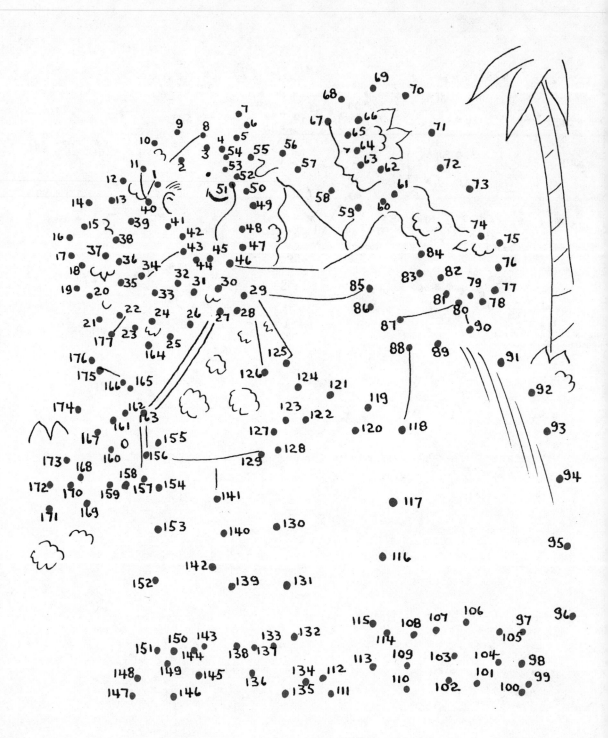

Round and Round

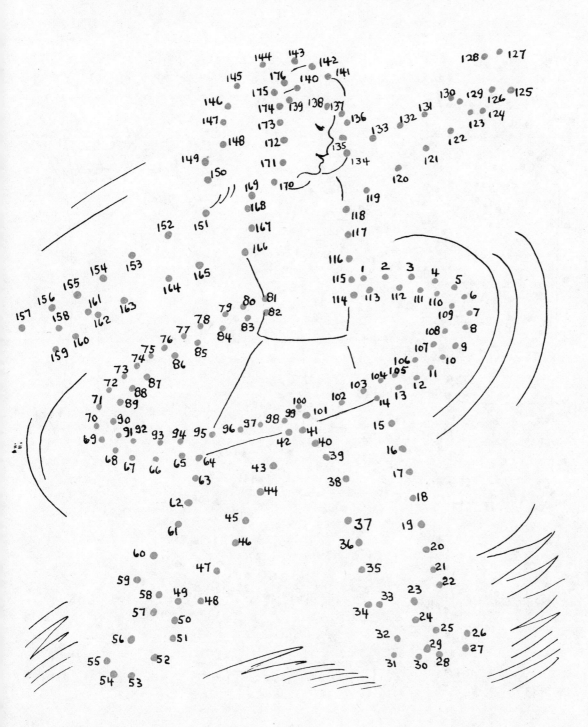

Whee!

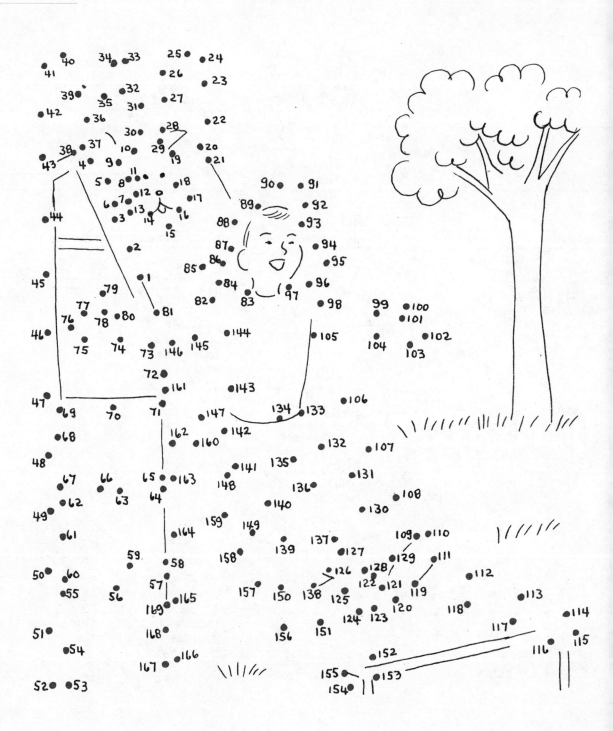

Big Appetite

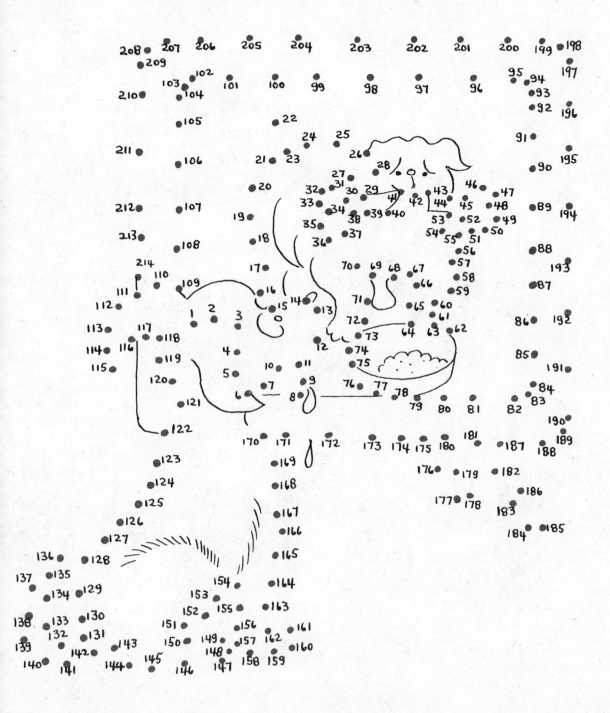

Party Fun

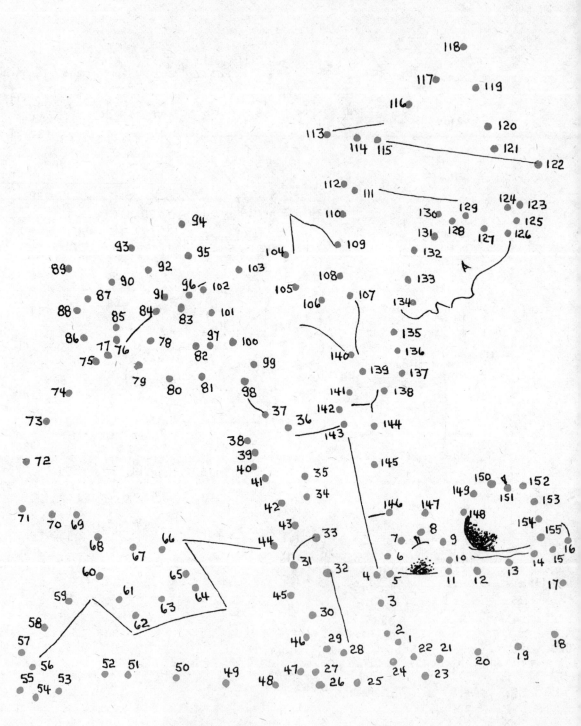

Not Too Good

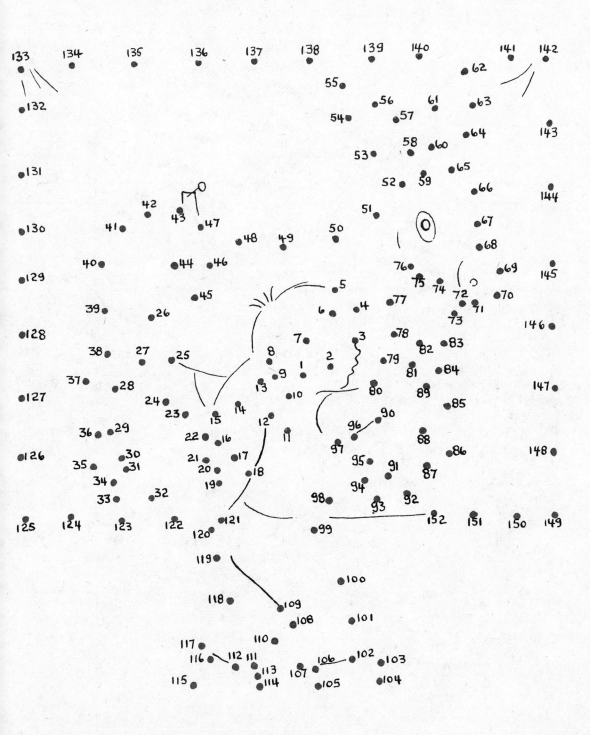

Let's Play

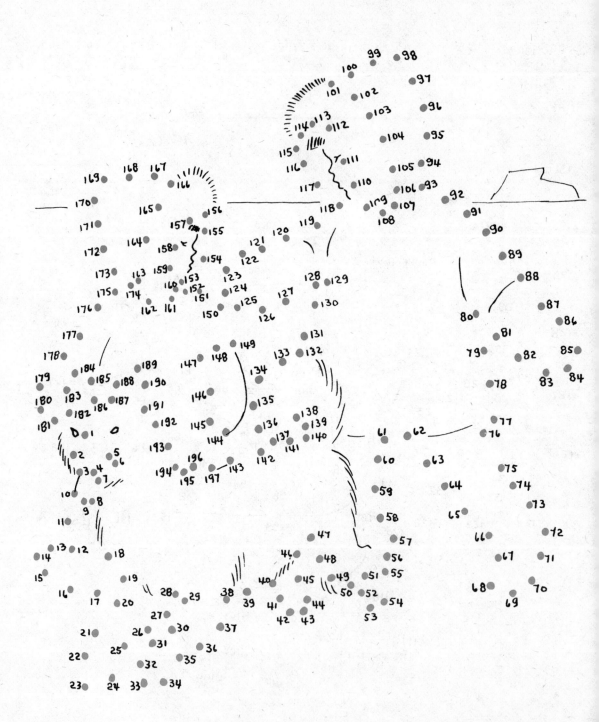

Stand Up!

109
108
107
110 106
116 113 111 105
115 112 100 101 104
114 99 102 103
117 98

122
123 121 120 119 118 97
124
125 96
127 126 95 52
128 89 51
88 87 53 42
129 90 50 43 41
86 91 93 94 57 54 55 49 44 40
85 92 58 56 48 45 39
130 59 60 61 47 46 38
62 37
131 84 63
82 81 35 36
132 83 80 79 68 64 34
133 69 65
78 70 71 66 33
135 134 72 67
136 157 158 159 160 181 73 32
137 155 156 182 180 77 74 31
138 153 154 152 179 76 75 30
139 151 150 161 1 2 4 10 19 20 21
140 149 162 3 5 9 11 18 22 29
141 148 163 178 8 6 7 12 17 23 28
146 164 167 168 177 16 24 26 27
142 165 166 170 169 176 13 15 25
143 144 145 171 172 173 174 175 14

69

Over the Top

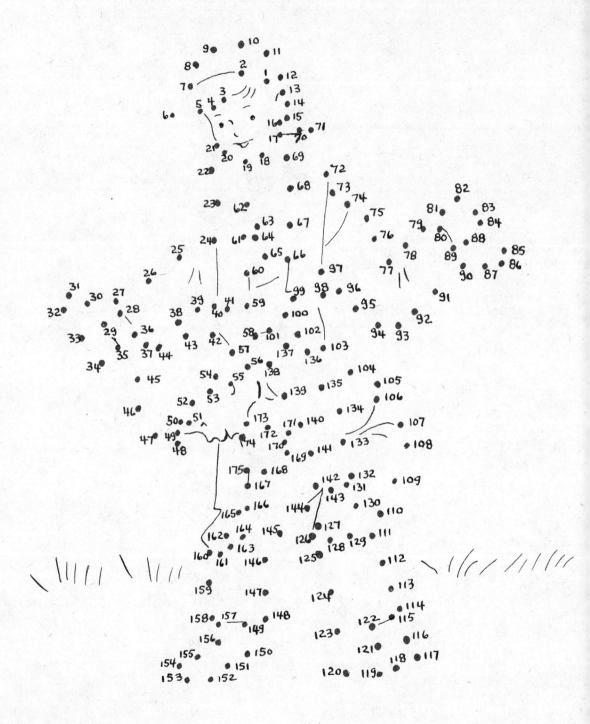

Bon Voyage

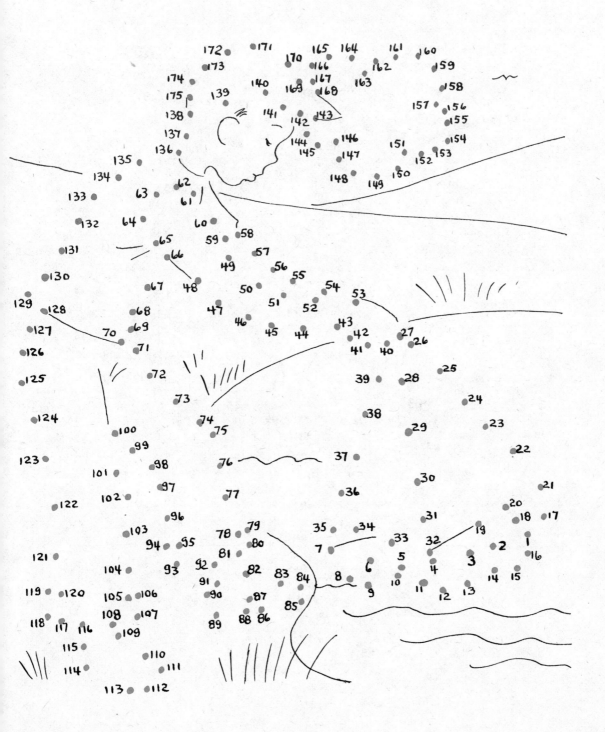

Right Through

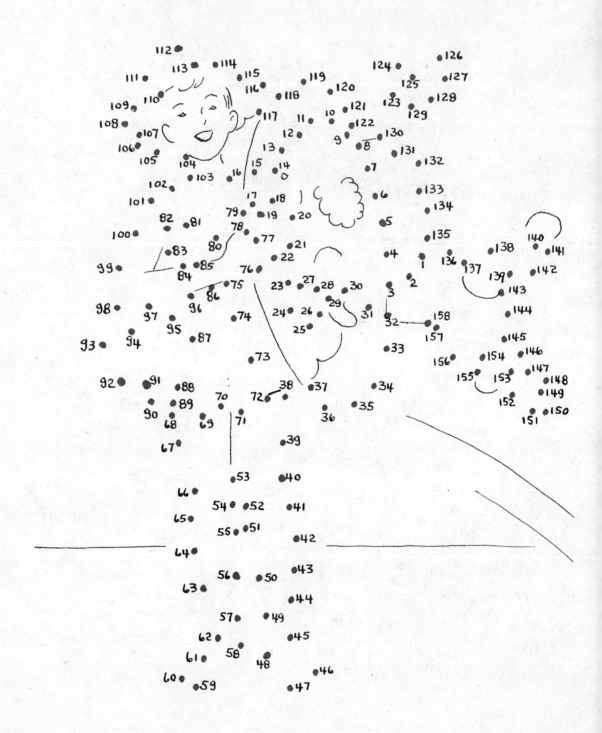

Midnight Raid

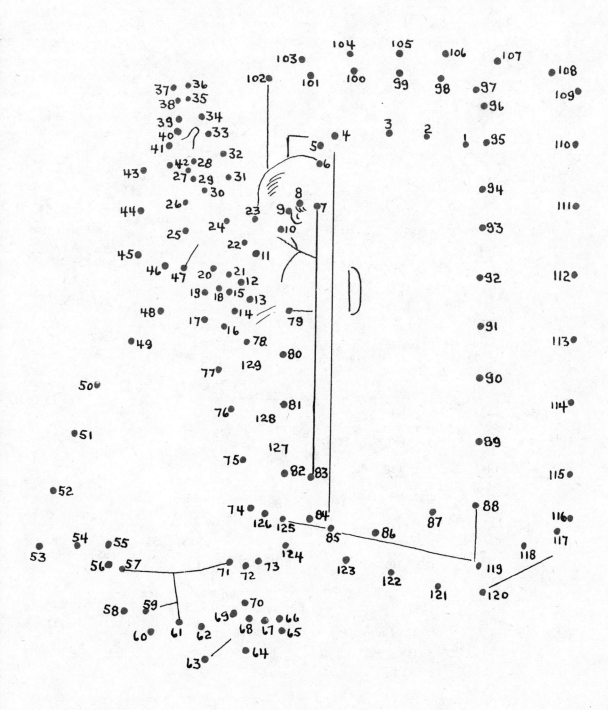

Good Fortune

Help!

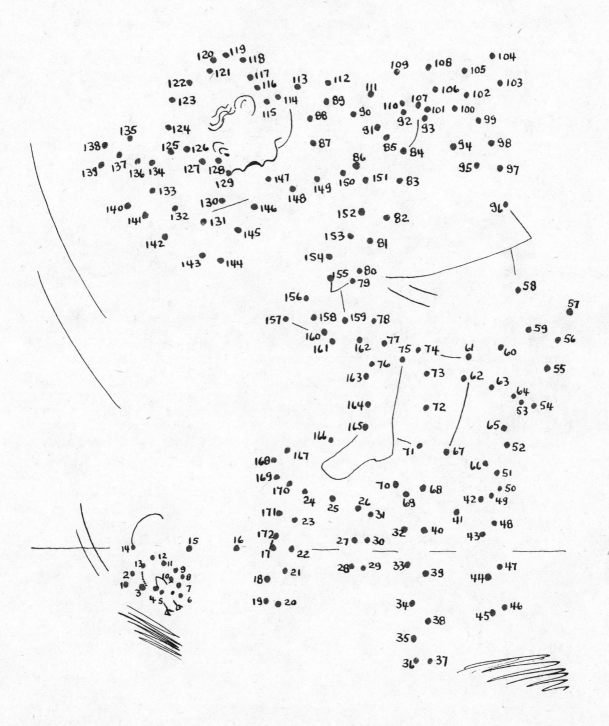

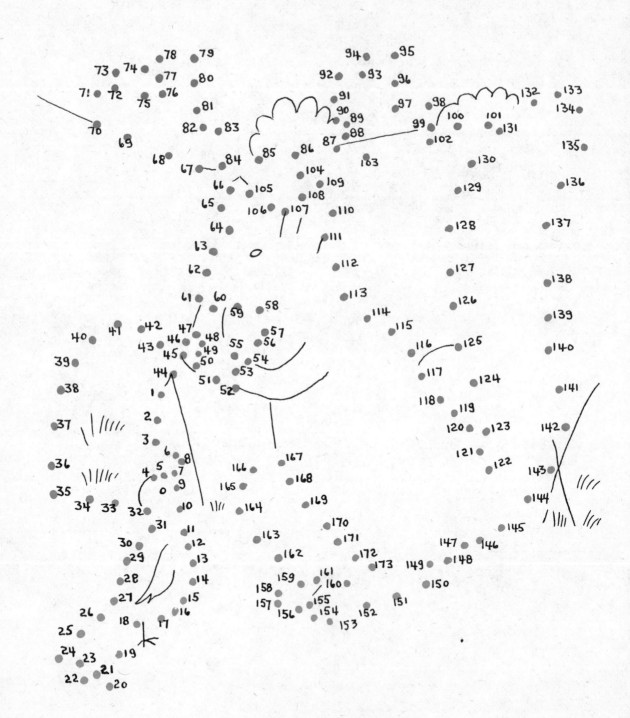

Watch My Smoke

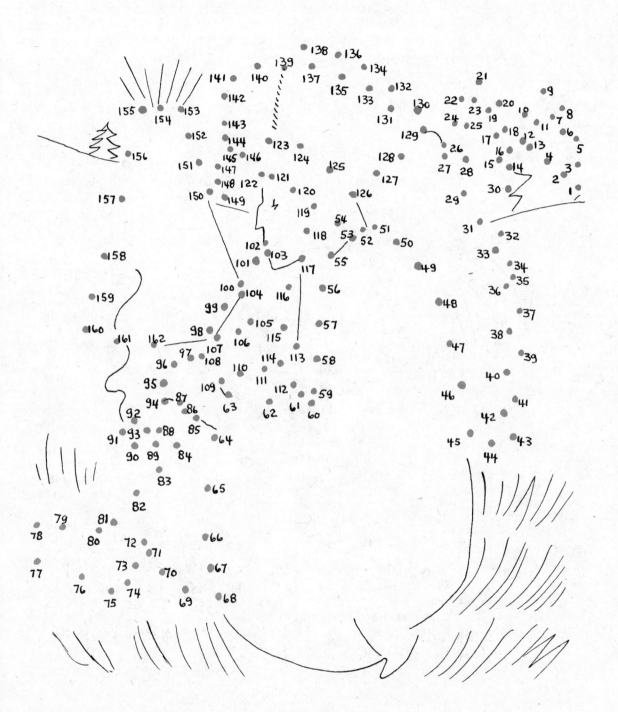

Creeping Along

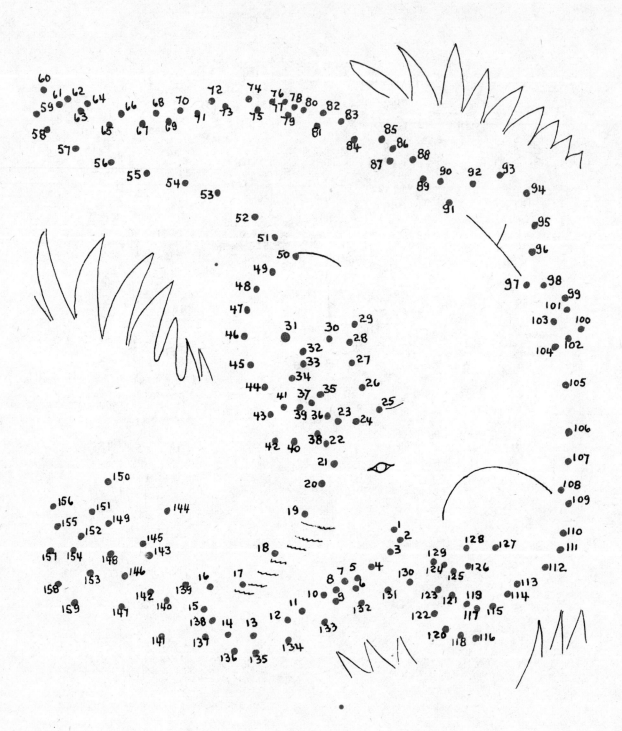

Air Travel

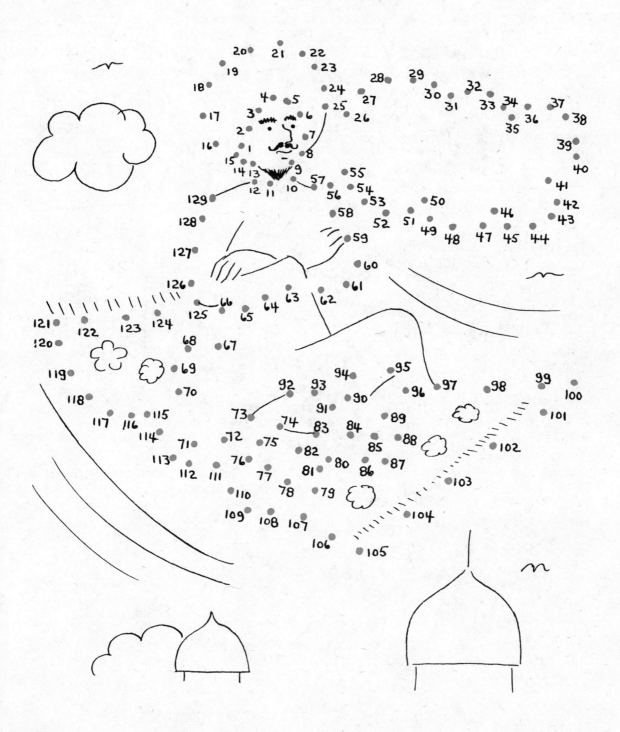

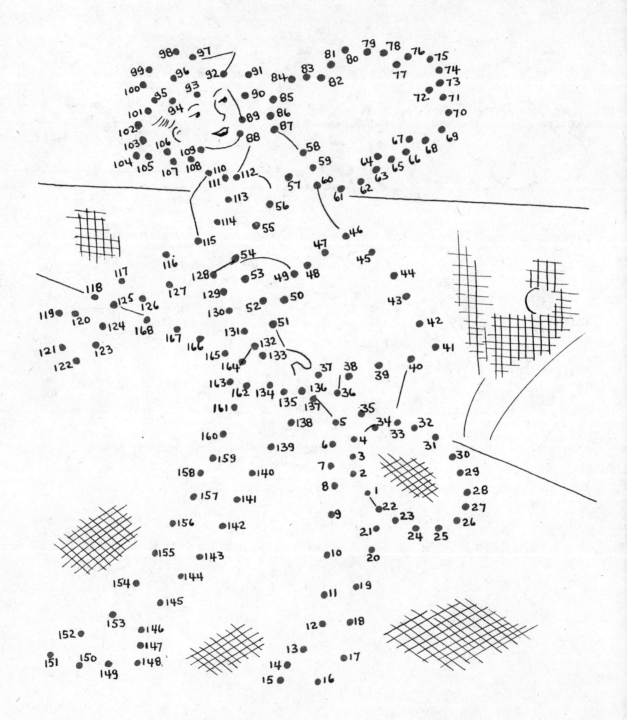

No Hands

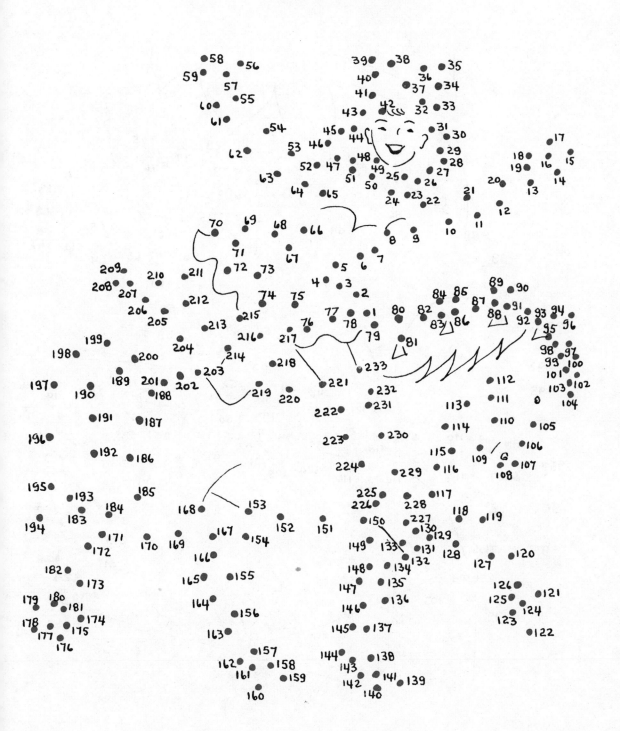

Please Go Away

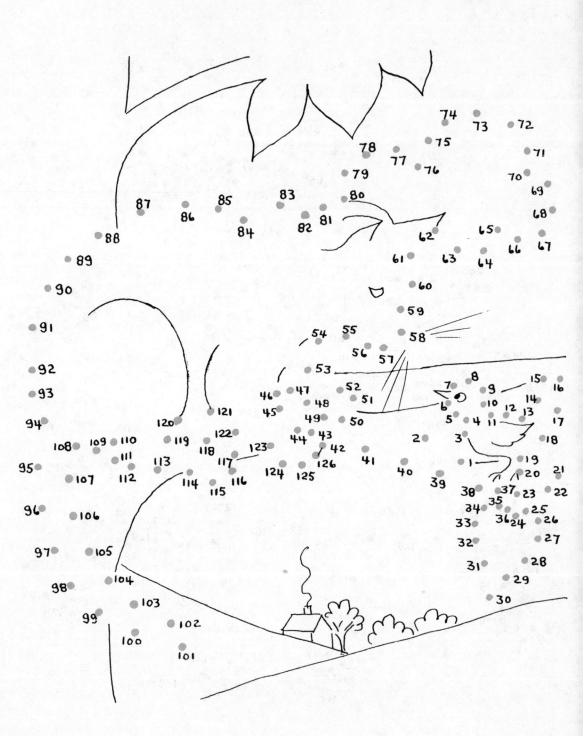

Interesting Story

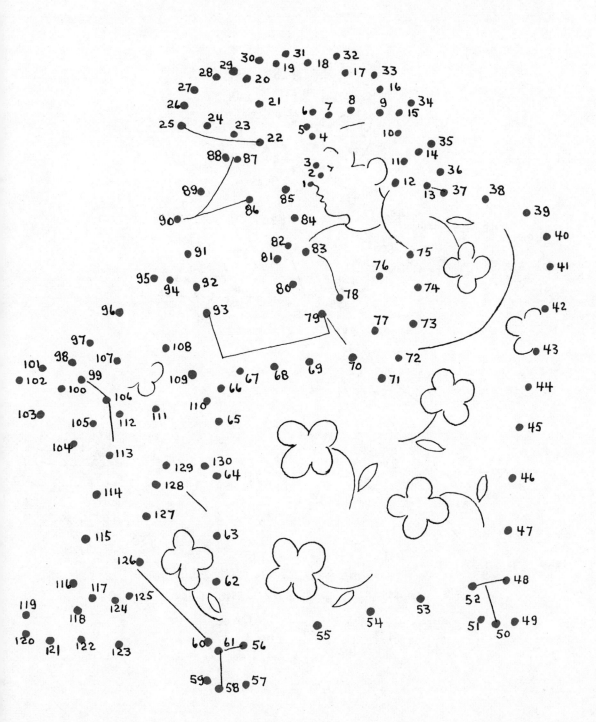

Fiesta

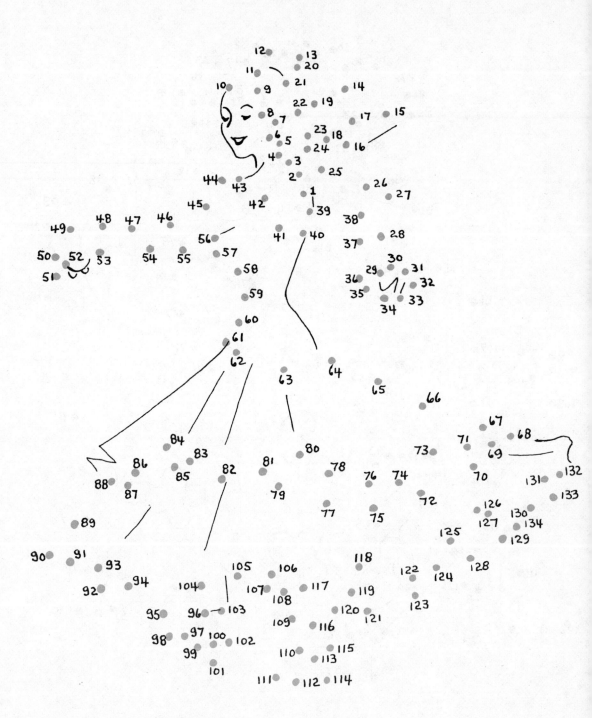

Is There Enough?

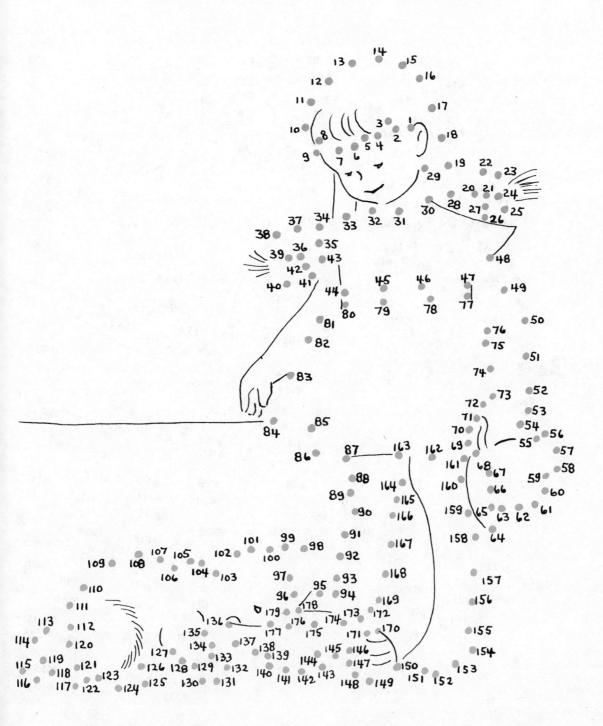

Here He Comes

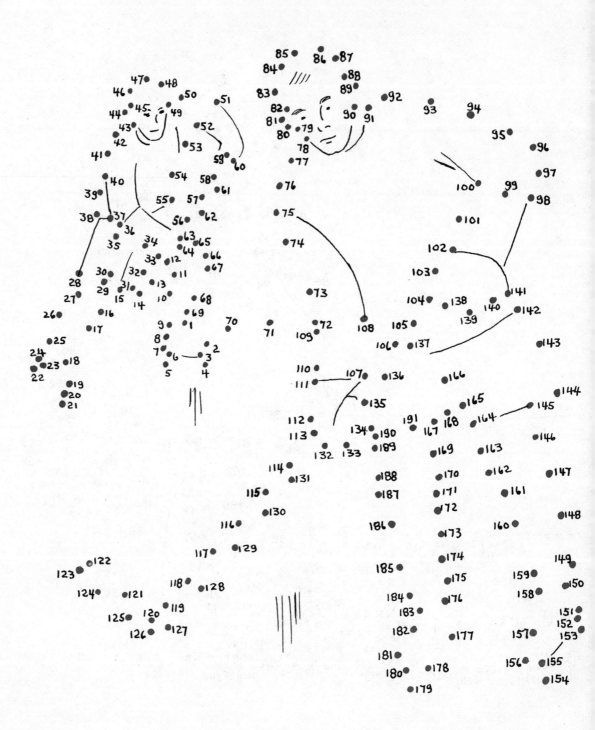

Hi There

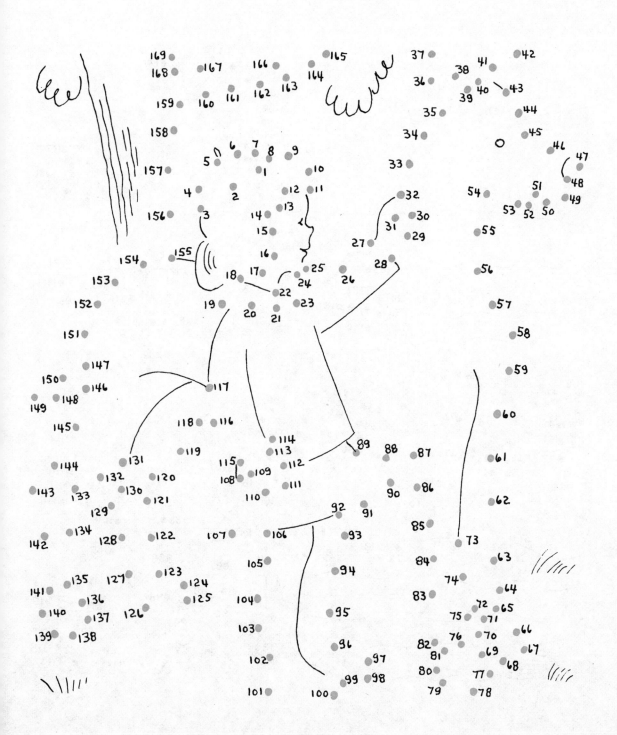

87

Hungry?

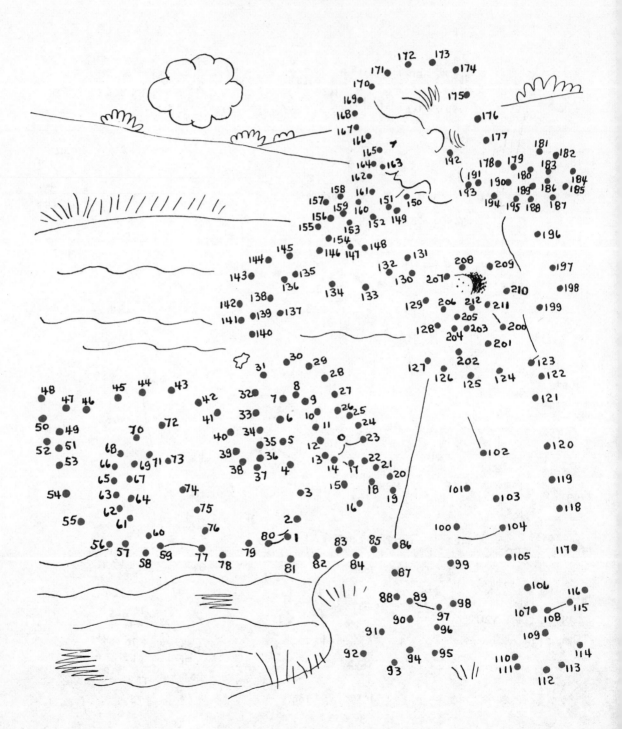

What's Wrong Now?

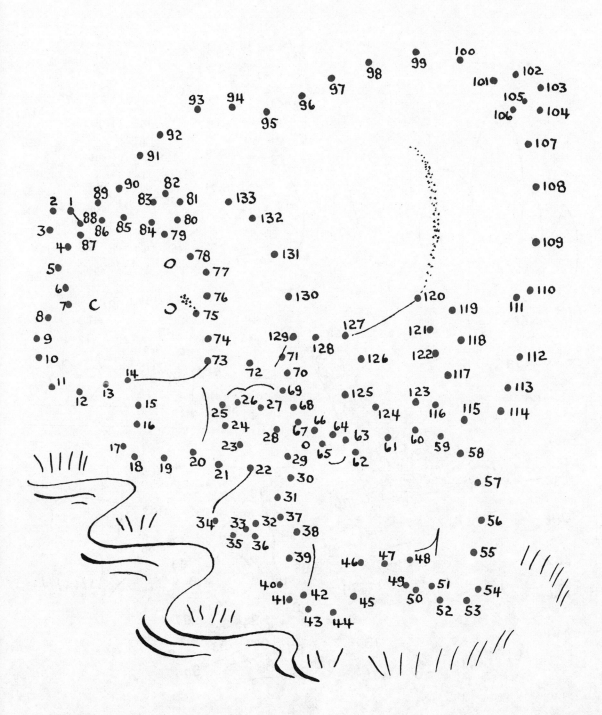

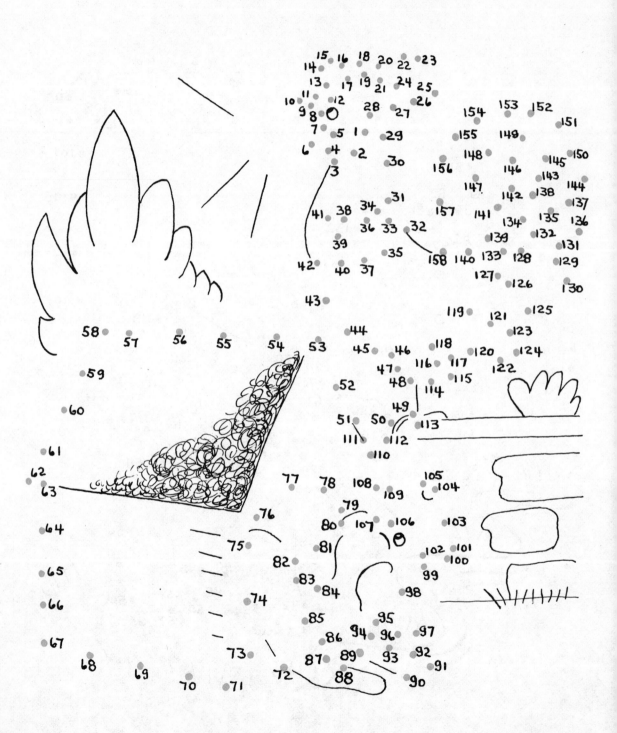

Follow Me!

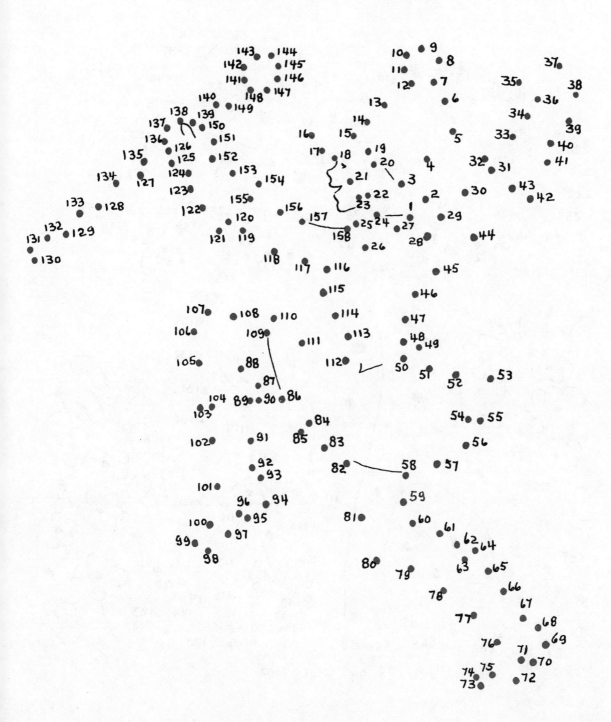

Mascot

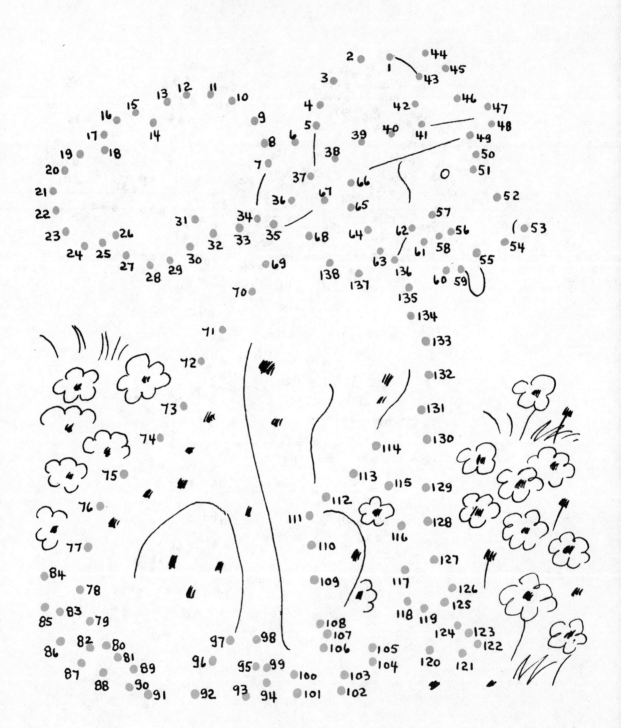

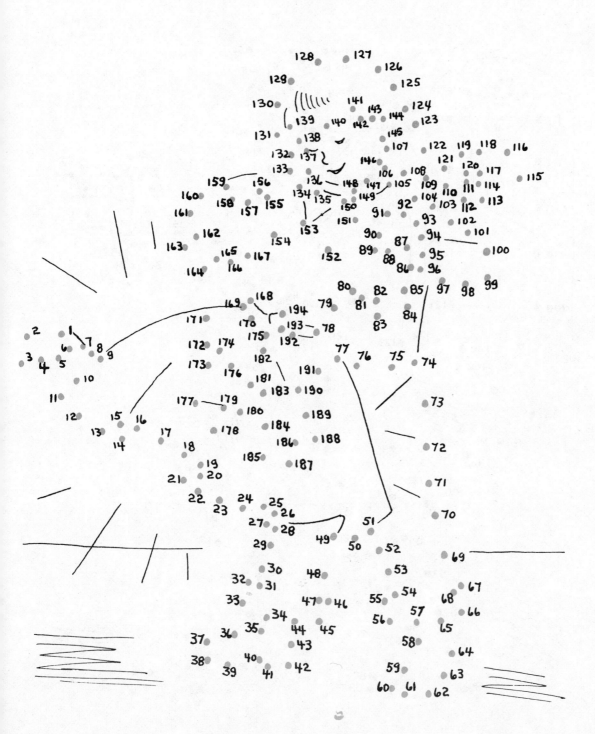

Court Scene

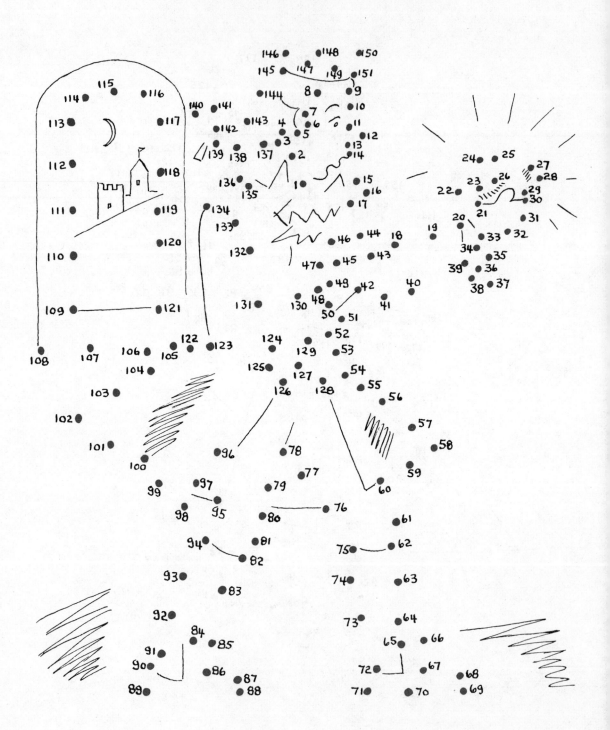

New Coat

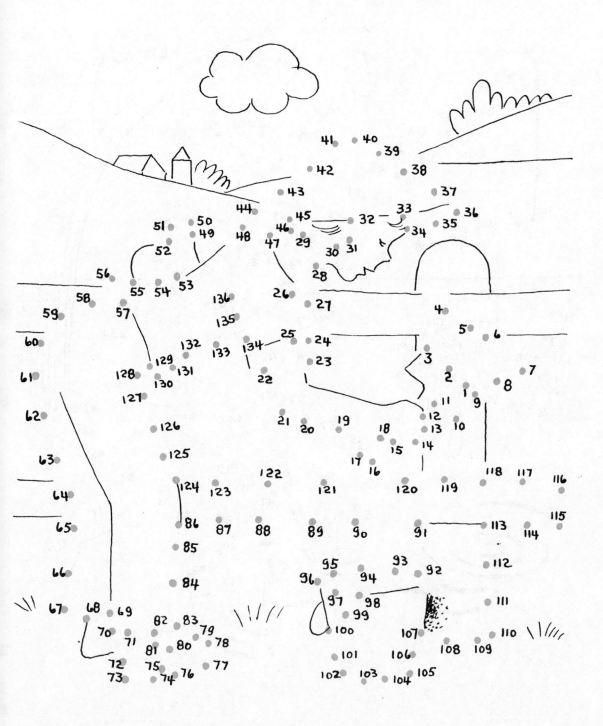

Disappointment

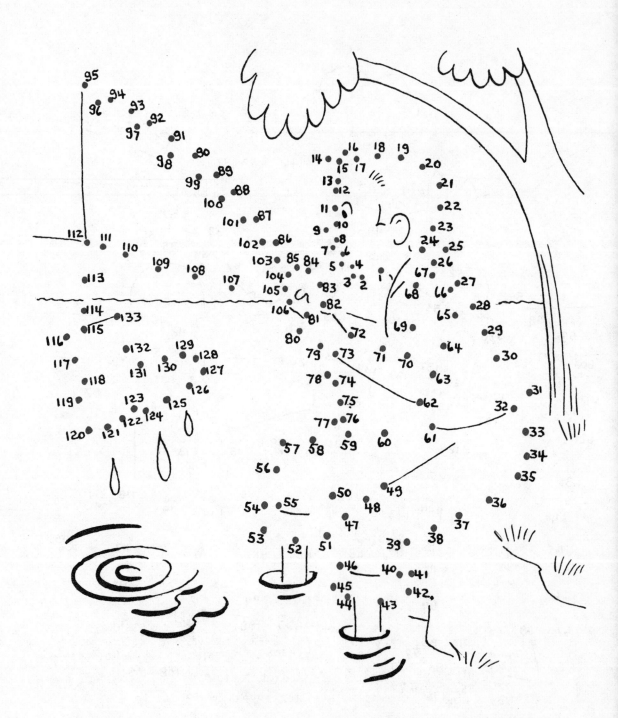

Sturdy Fellow

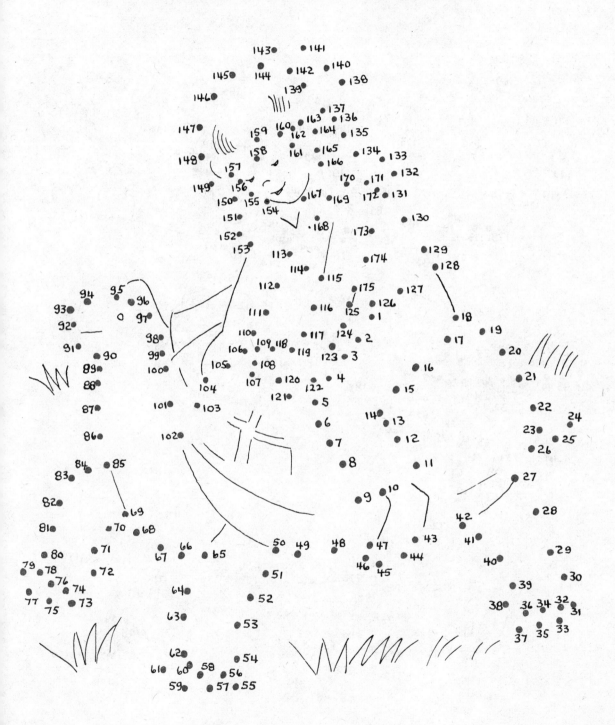

Nursery Rhyme

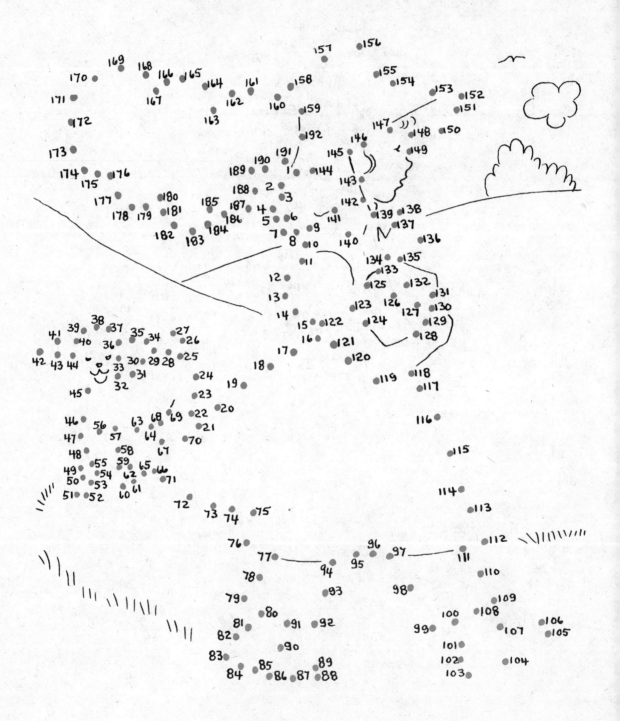

Good Butter

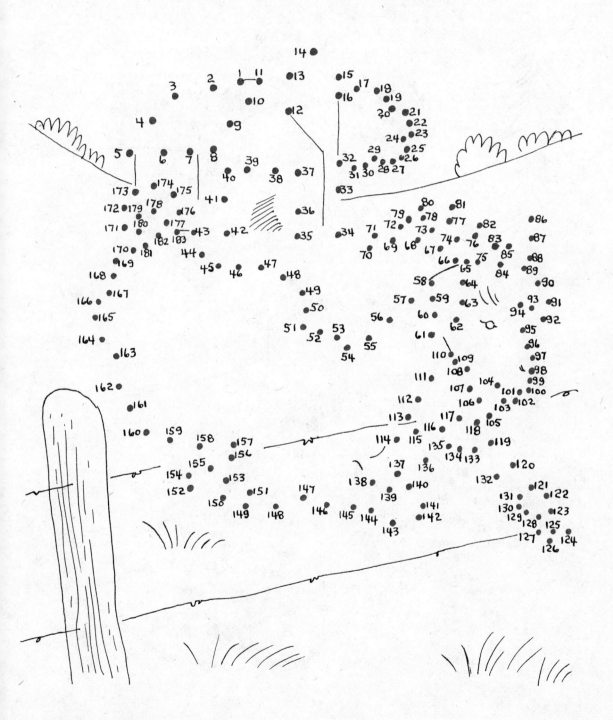

Winter Hike

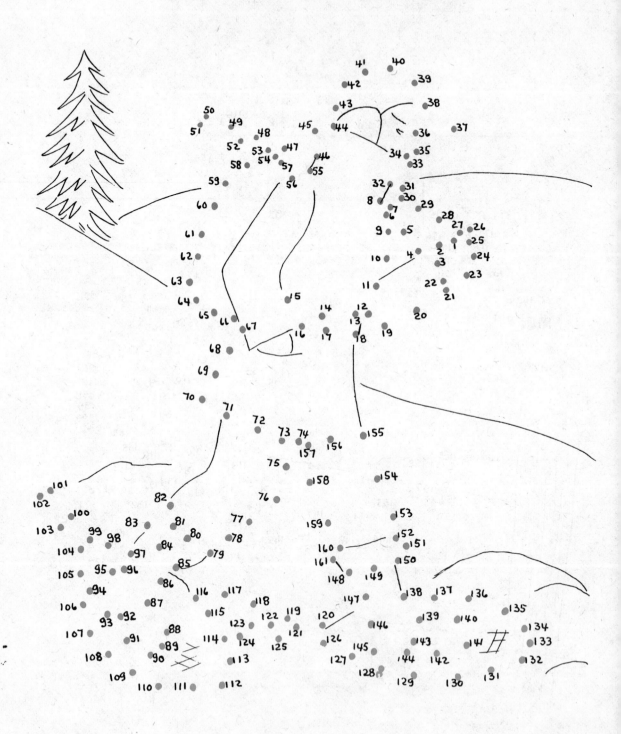

April Day

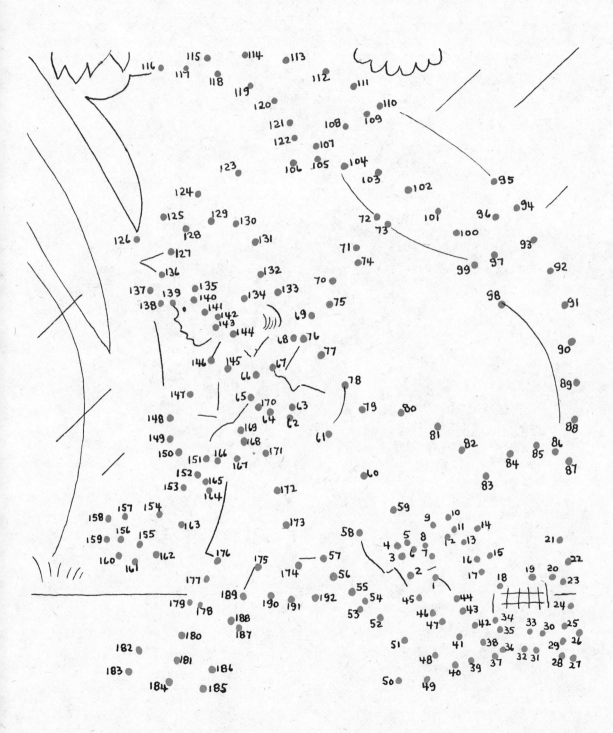

Take Off

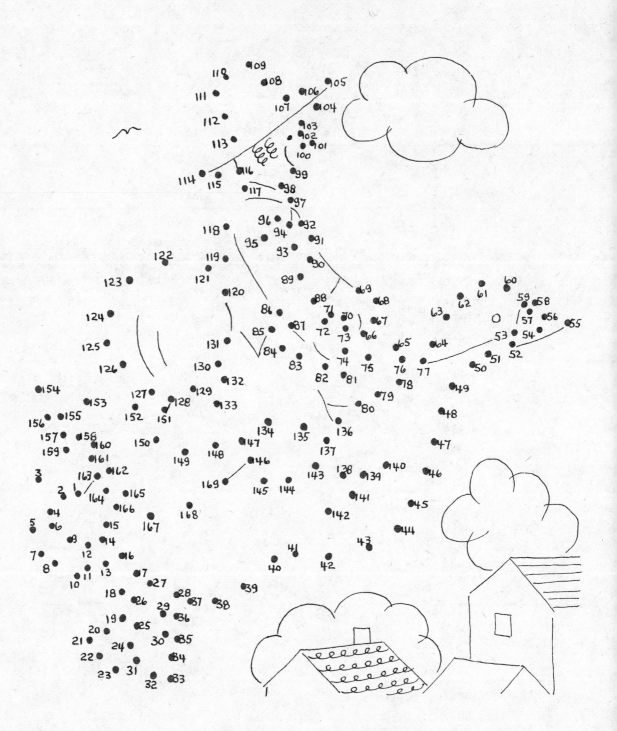

Take That!

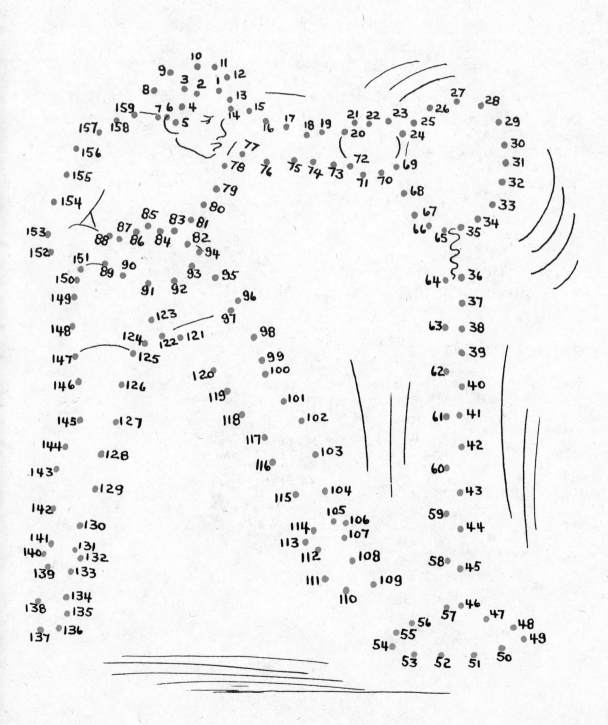

Only Me

Learning How

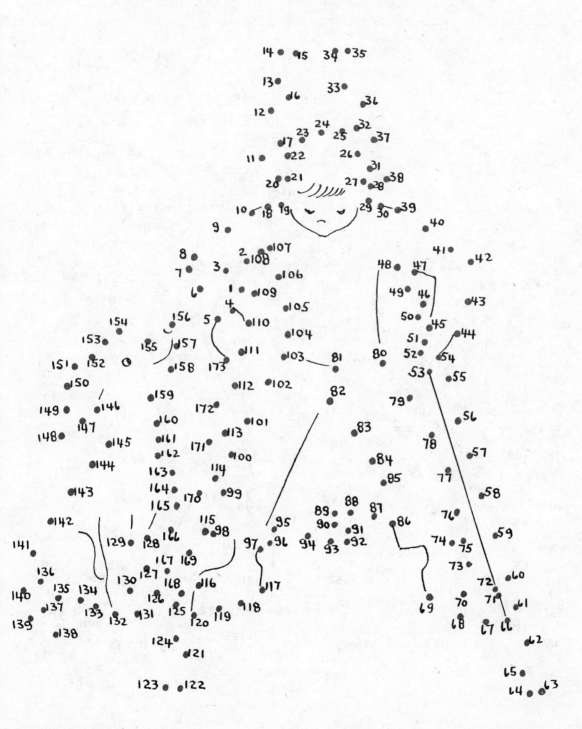

Giddyap!

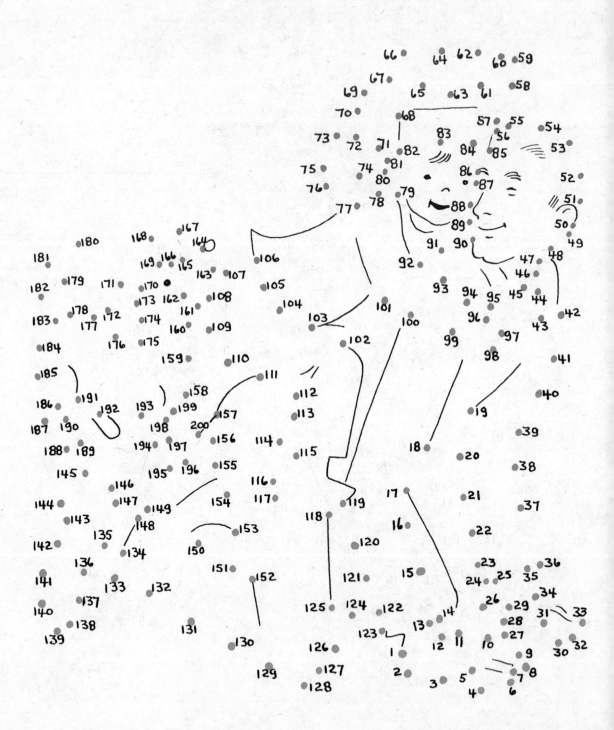

Going Down

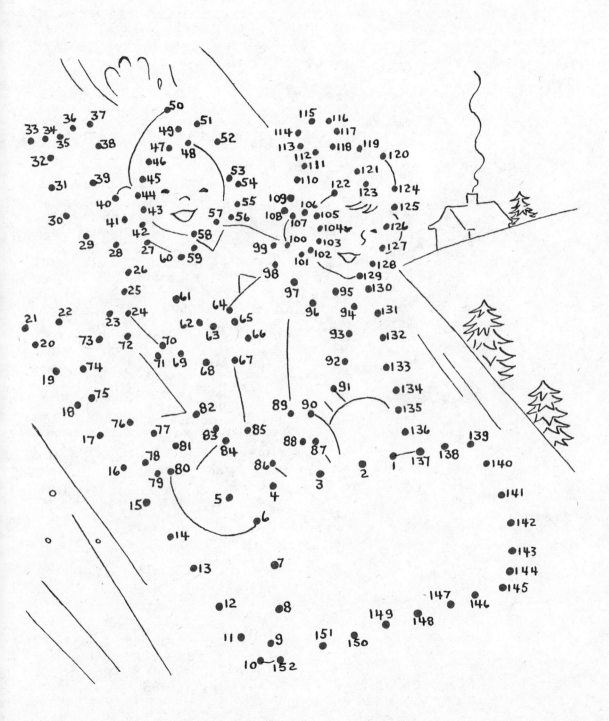

Halloween

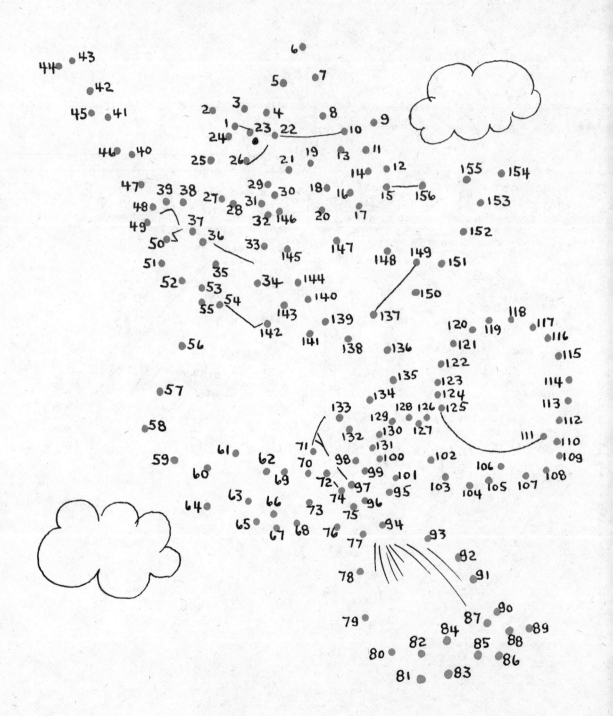

108

Fairy Tale

82
84
81 83 85 86
87
88
80 89
124 125 127
122 123 126 128 129
121 114 112 130
66 67 79 120 119 115 113 111 110 131
65 68 117 109 132
64 69 90 118 116 108 133
63 70 78 91
62 71 77 93 98 107 106 134
61 72 73 74 92 94 96 105 135
60 75 181 178 95 97 99 104 136
20 18 17 76 180 177 137
21 19 179 176 100 101 138
23 22 15 16 173 175 166 102 103 145
59 14 172 174 167 165 164 146 144 139
24 25 13 171 169 168 163 147 143
58 57 26 12 11 9 8 6 170 162 155 154 148 142 140
56 27 1 10 7 5 161 156 141
55 2 3 4 32 160 159 153 149
28 158 157 152 150
29 30 31 33 151
54
34
52 36 35
53 51 45 37
46 44 38
50 47 43 39
49 48 42 41 40

109

Old Venice

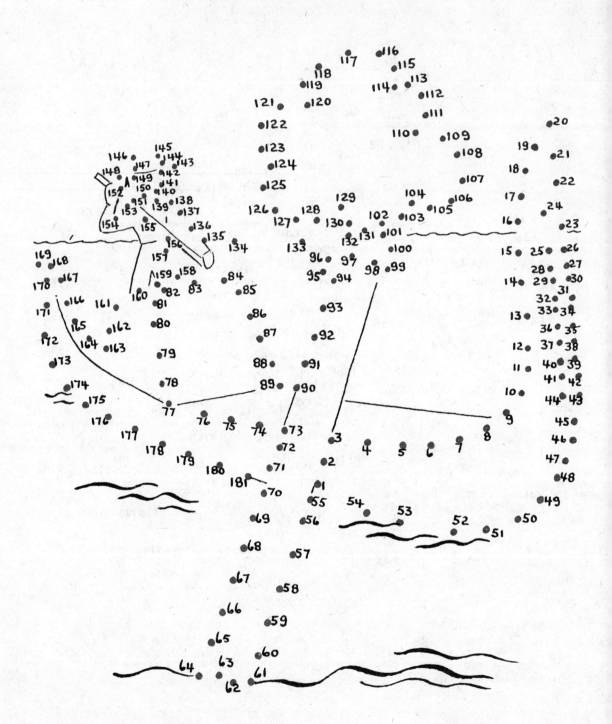

Across the Desert

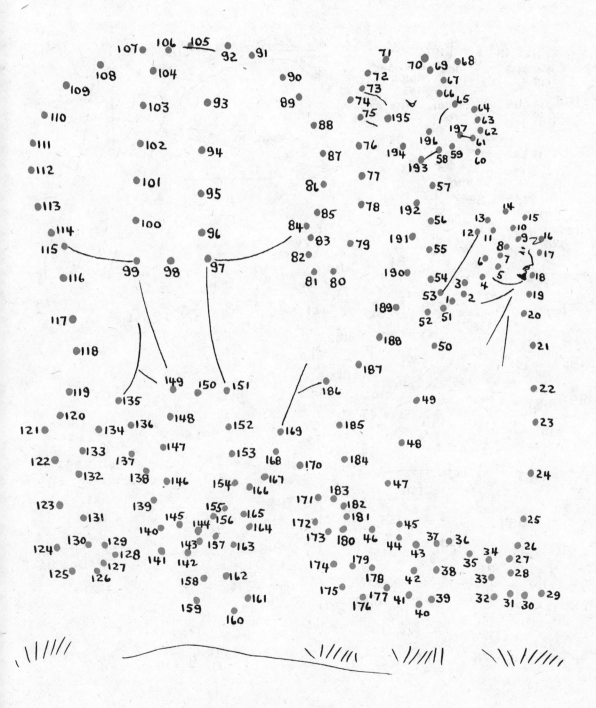

Rolling Along

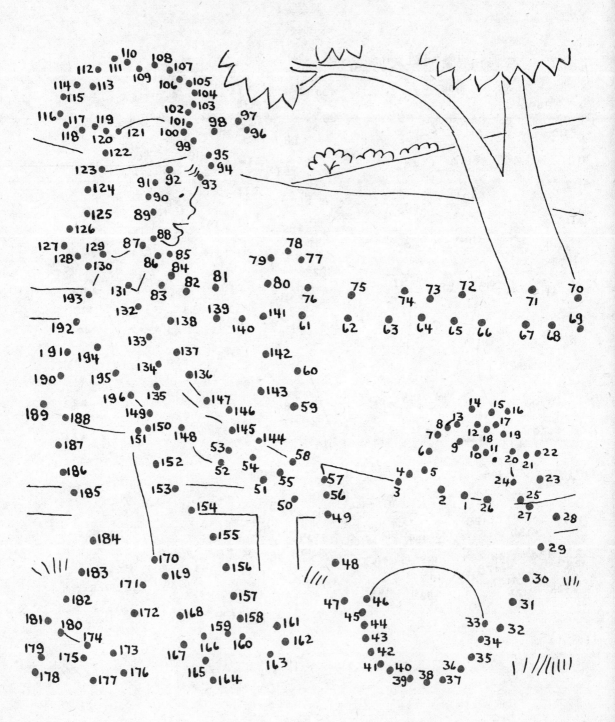

Pull Hard

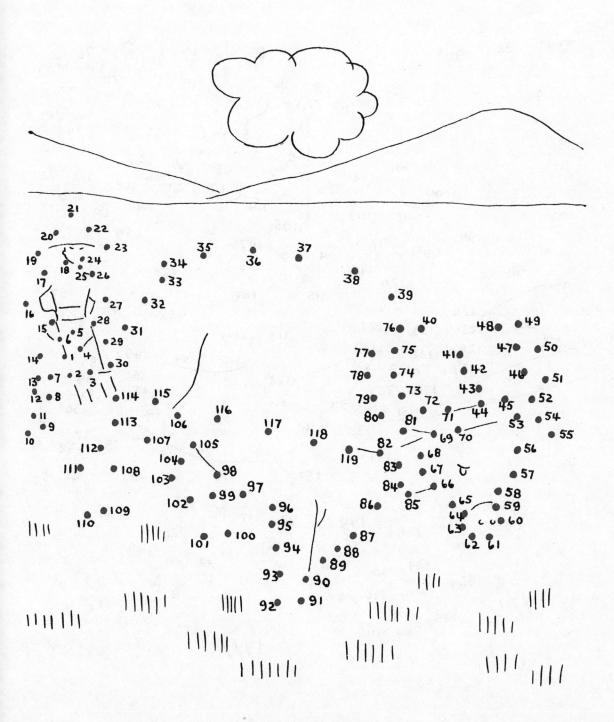

Windy Day

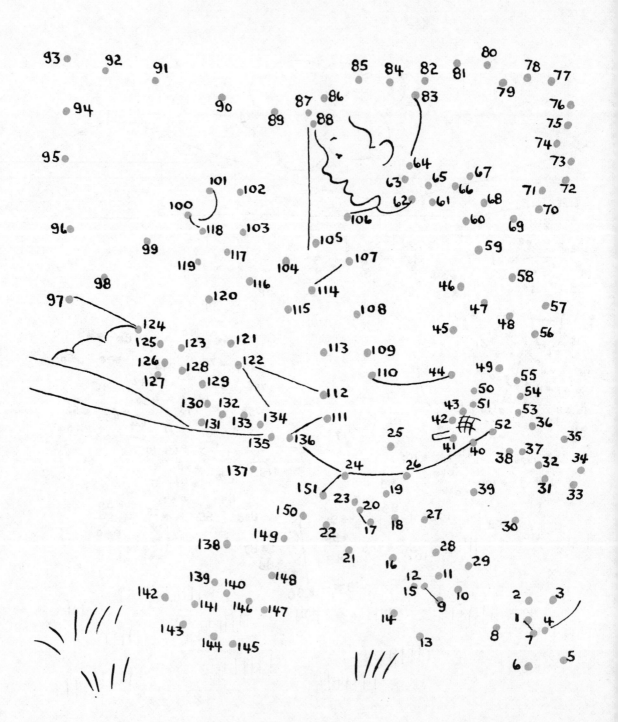

Hang on Tight

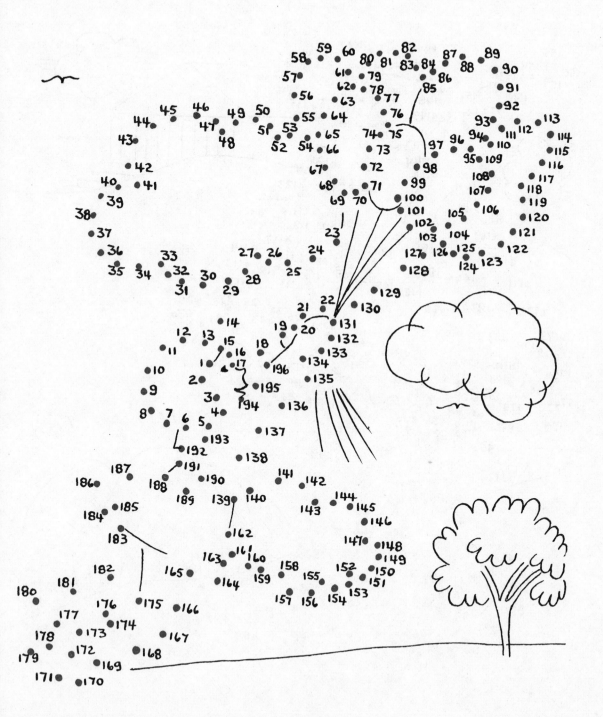

Ancient Land

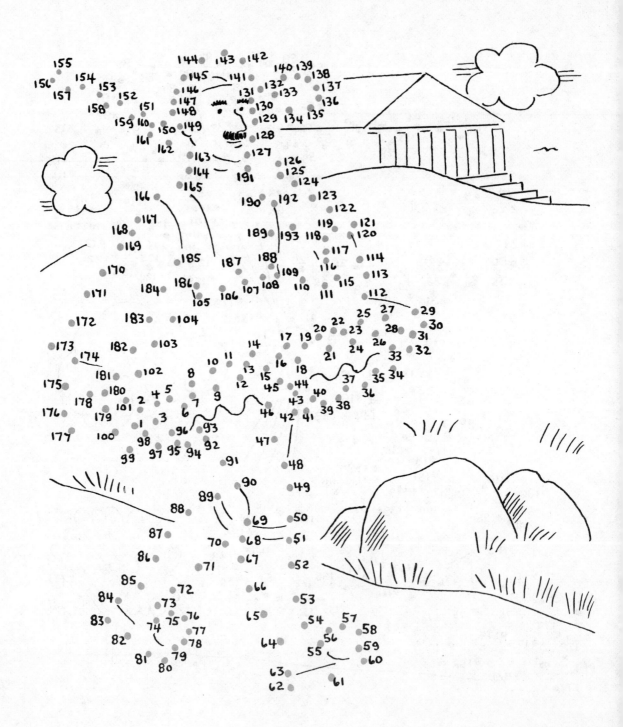

Back Yard Fun

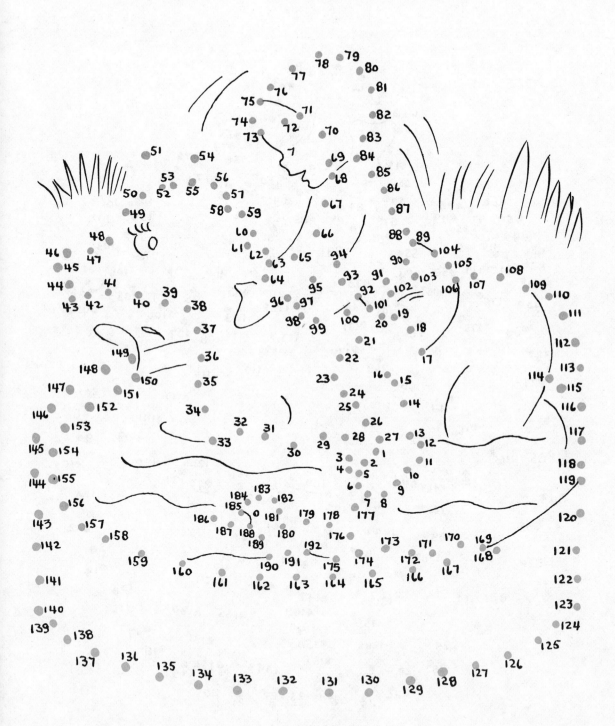

How Many Times?

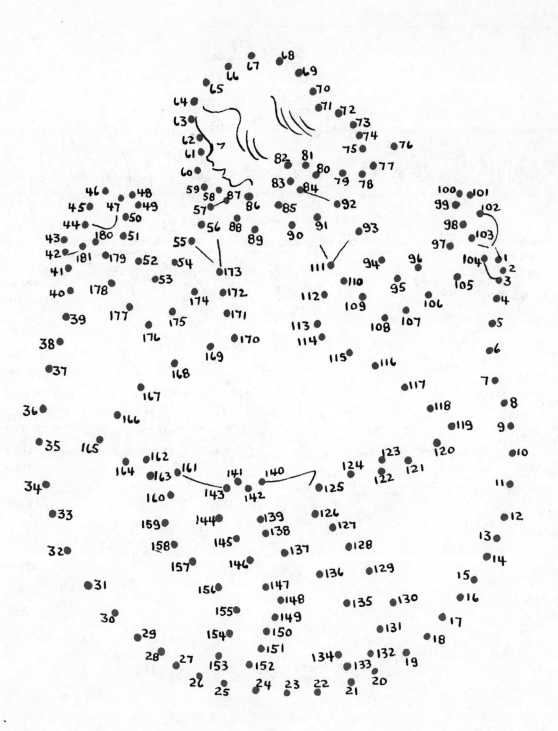

Shopping Spree

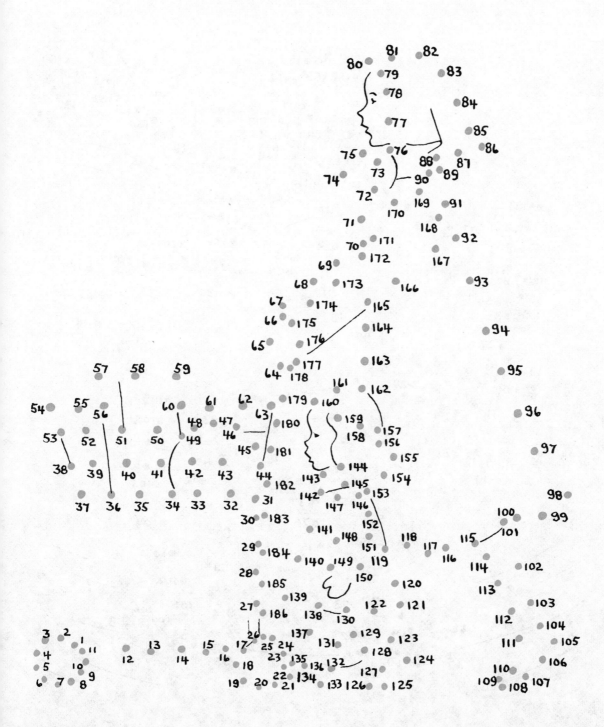

Dangerous Walk

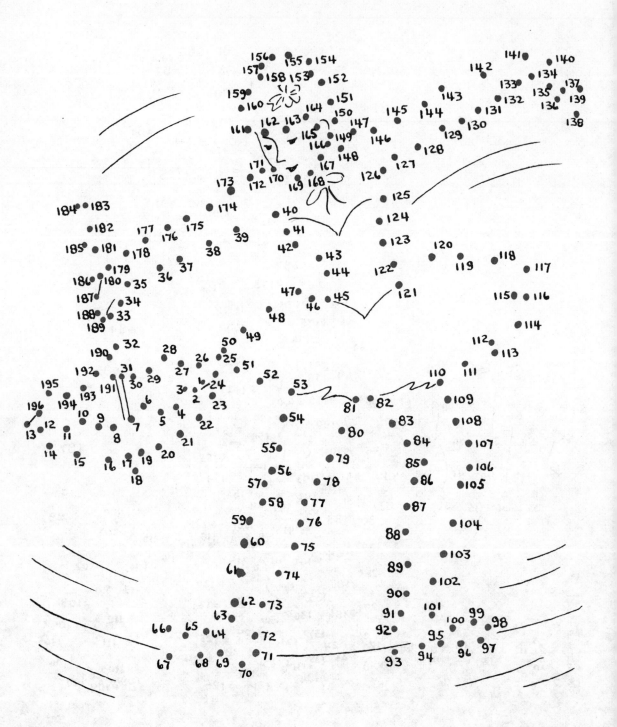

Speed Demon

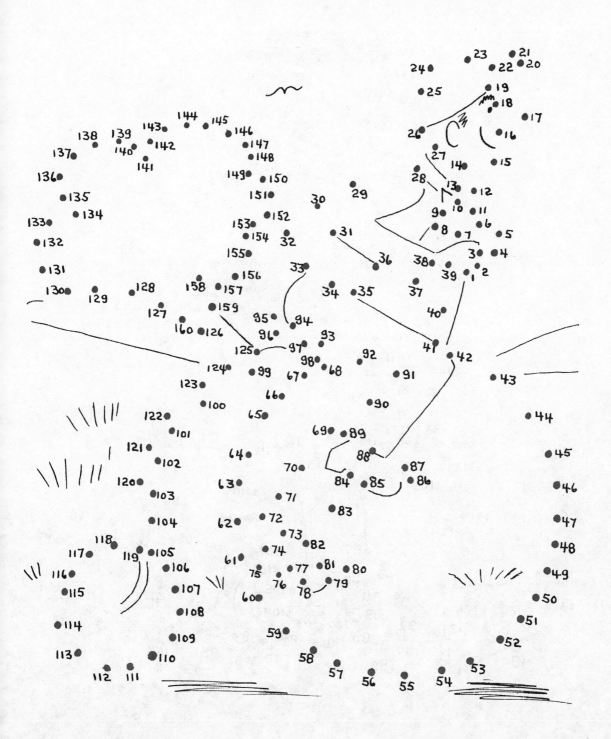

Mother's Helper

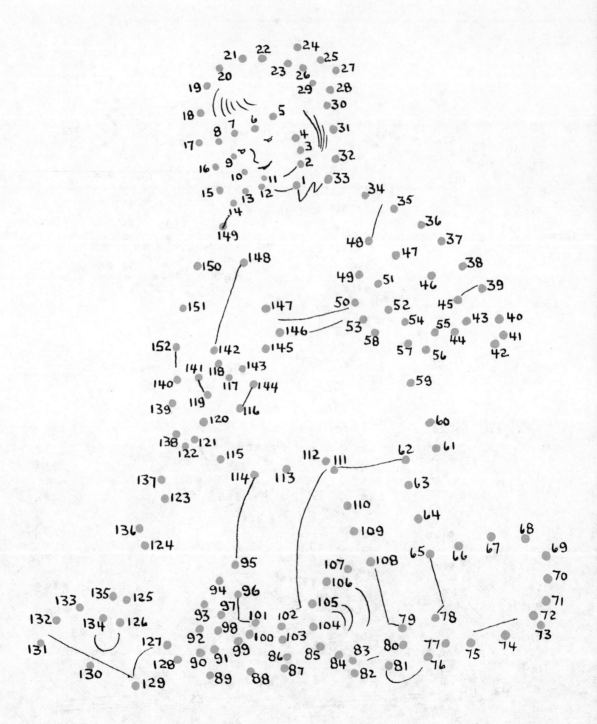

Going My Way?

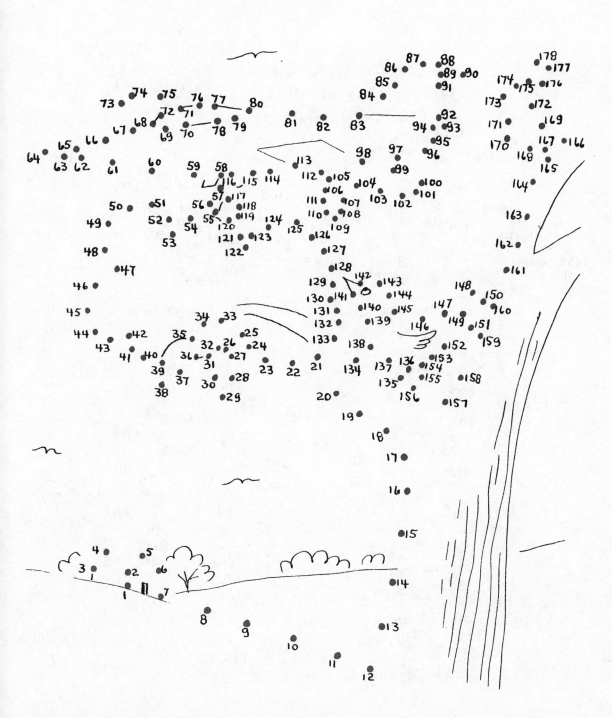

In the Woods

124 • 124

130
125 123
131 126 122 121
137 129 127 118 120
132 128 117 119
138 136 133 116
139 134 115 100 97
140 135 112 109 103 101 98
142 141 114 113 111 110 108 104 99 96
143 8 7 6 107 106 105 102 95
145 18 9 5 4 3 94
144 17 10 1 2 93
146 20 19 16 12 11 92
21 15 13
22 14 91
23 76
24 75 60 90
25 59 74 77 89
26 58 61 78 88
42 57 62 73 79
27 56 72 81
63 80
28 41 55 64 71 81 86
29 40 43 54 65 70 82 85
30 44 45 66 69 84
39 67 68 83
31 38 46 53
32 37 47 52
33 36 48 51
34 35 49 50

124

Western Scene

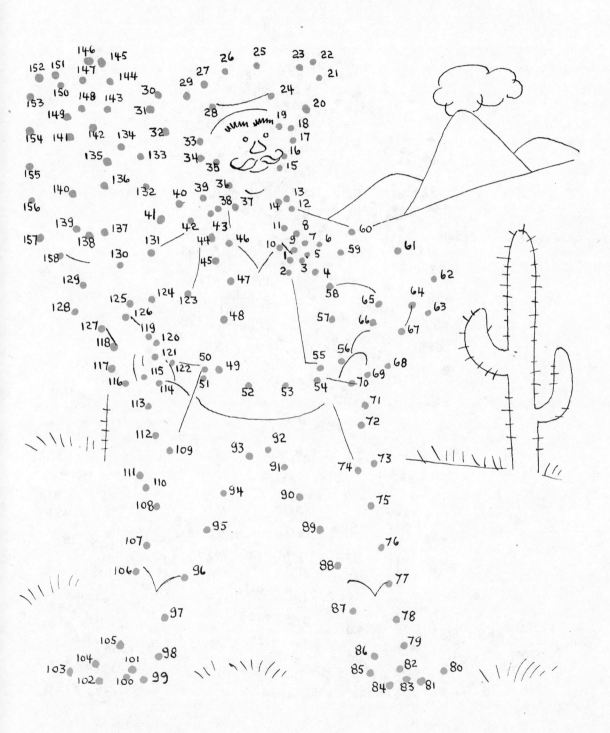

Step Lively!

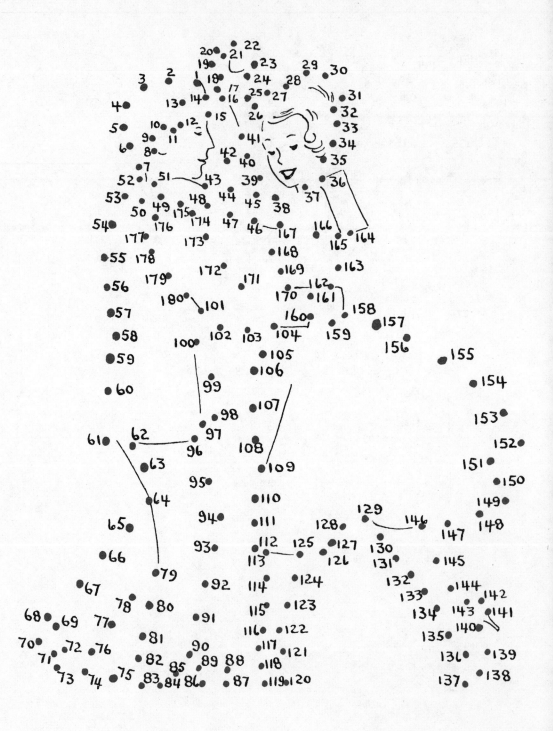

Swinging High

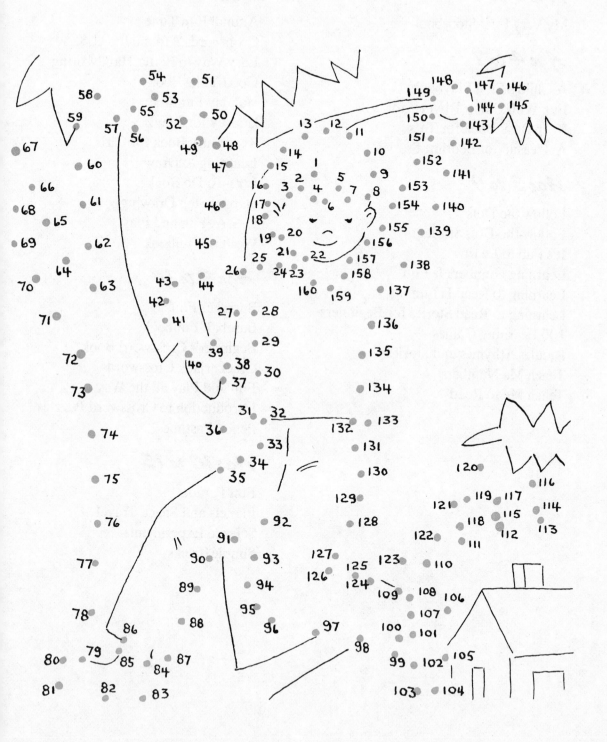

Doubleday Activity Books

Age 2 to 4

My Very First Storybook

Age 4 to 7

A Child's First Playbook
Fun With Dots—Rhymes for Tots
Keep Busy Book for Tots
A Treasury of Bedtime Stories

Age 5 to 9

Follow the Dots
Follow-the-Dots Stories
It's Fun to Learn
Learning Numbers Is Fun
Learning to Read Is Fun
Learning to Read Stories for Beginners
100 Learning Games
Riddles, Rhymes and Stories
Teach Me Numbers
Teach Me to Read

Age 7 to 11

Animal Fun Time
Crosswords Around the U.S.A.
Easy Way to Better Handwriting
Good Time Book
Holiday Funtime
Hooray for Play!
Keep Busy Book for Girls
Learning to Draw
Lots-To-Do Book
Step by Step Drawing
U.S.A. Fun and Play
Western Funbook

Age 9 to 14

Barrel of Fun
Baseball Funbook
Beginner's Crossword Book
Crackerjack Crosswords
Fun and Play all the Way
Introduction to Crossword Puzzles
Pencil Pastimes

Age 10 to 15

Fun Parade
Planets and Space Travel
Science Experiments
Simple Tricks